THE BEATLES FOR CLASSICAL GUITAR

20 SOLOS ARRANGED BY JOE WASHINGTON

WISE PUBLICATIONS
London/New York/Sydney

Exclusively distributed by:
Music Sales Limited,
78 Newman Street,
London, W1P 3LA, England

Music Sales PTY Limited,
27 Clarendon Street,
Artarmon,
Sydney, N.S.W.,
Australia

Australian-born JOE WASHINGTON is
well-known as a teacher and arranger
for the Classical Guitar.

He studied music from an early age
and by the time he reached fifteen was
already a semi-professional. He studied
composition at the Sydney Conservatorium
of Music, and has written theme music for
television programmes as well as for
documentary films. He was also staff
arranger for Australian Broadcasting.

Although he plays many instruments, it
is the Guitar which has claimed most of
his attention. He is deeply interested in
its popular application, especially for
playing arrangements of music of the
great Groups, such as The Beatles.

CONTENTS

This Album © Copyright 1974 by
WISE PUBLICATIONS
London/New York/Sydney

FOREWORD

Many feel that the charm of the "Classical" Guitar should not be confined to what is usually called its "concert repertoire", this being beyond their scope and ambition. The aim of this book is to preserve this character while adapting it to today's popular music.

It will be seen that the first few solos are simple, and so that those with poor reading ability will be able to play them, a system based on Chord Diagrams has been developed. This method covers all the notes in the arrangements and is fully described in the section titled "THE STRATA SYSTEM".

A section called READING GUITAR MUSIC has been included. A study of this, together with the experience gained in playing the first few solos, should enable one to continue. The later solos, because of the need of fuller musical notation, are too complicated for the Strata System but with a little application most should be within reach.

Each arrangement has an accompanying set of instructions dealing with possible difficulties. These also contain general observations which may be of interest even to those whose reading ability may need no assistance.

The desire on the part of many to know about hand-positions, and the need for general information on the Technique of the "classical" guitar has led me to include the section CLASSICAL GUITAR TECHNIQUE at the back of the book.

Most of these arrangements were done for my pupils and it was because of our mutual enjoyment that I was encouraged to have them published.

Finally, I wish to express my indebtedness to J. McNaghten, who acted as Literary Editor; and Karl Schurr as Technical Editor.

Joe Washington

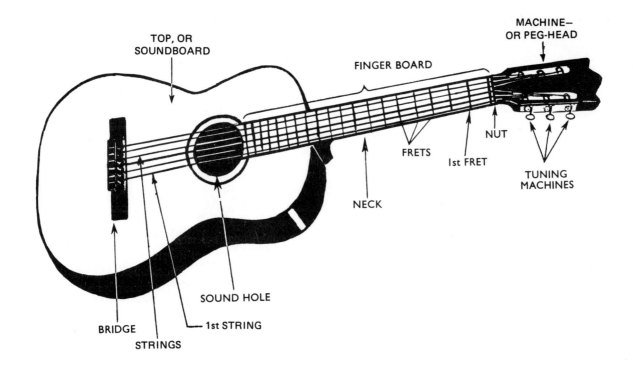

The "Classical", or "Finger-style" guitar is constructed so as to respond to *Nylon strings*. Steel strings must not be used as they impose too great a strain on the sound-board.

To attempt to learn "classical" technique while using a "Jumbo" type guitar (with or without nylon strings) is inappropriate since this generally has a narrow neck — consequently having the strings more closely-spaced — and is more suited to strumming and the use of a plectrum.

Many suitable models of "classical" guitar are available at almost every price-level, and *the first essentials* are:
1. The fingerboard (fret-board) should be *flat* — sight along its edge from the nut to the end near the soundhole.
2. Its "action" should be satisfactory — the strings lying close enough to the fingerboard to be pressed down easily by the left-hand fingers, but not low enough to "buzz" against the frets at any point.
3. The *"harmonic"* at the 12th fret should be in tune with the *note* at that fret.
4. Overall *width across the strings* should be *at least* 4.5 cm. (1¾") at the nut, and 5.8 cm. (2¼") at the bridge.

SIGNS USED IN GUITAR MUSIC

a) A number in a circle indicates the string e.g.
⑤ = 5th string

b) Right hand fingering indicated by letters
 p – pulgar – thumb
 i – indice – 1st finger (index)
 m – medio – 2nd finger
 a – anular – 3rd finger

c) Left hand fingering indicated by numbers
 1 – 1st finger (index)
 2 – 2nd finger
 3 – 3rd finger
 4 – little finger
 o – open string

d) A Roman numeral indicates position, (i.e. the position taken by the left hand on the fingerboard with the first finger at a certain fret).

I   1st position, means to place the hand so that the 1st finger is at the 1st fret with the other fingers ready to be placed at frets 2, 3 and 4.

V   – 5th position – 1st finger at the 5th fret, and other fingers ready at frets 6, 7 and 8.

Guitar music is written in the Treble Clef, an octave (eight notes) higher than the sound produced.

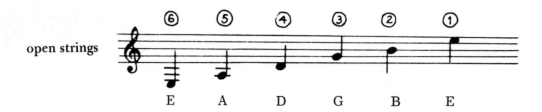

open strings

E   A   D   G   B   E

Place a Finger of the left hand at the 5th fret of the 6th string making the note A and tune the open 5th string in unison with it.
Stop the 5th fret of the 5th string making note D and tune 4th string to it.
Stop the 5th fret of the 4th string making note G and tune 3rd string to it.

Stop the 4th fret of the 3rd string making note B and tune 2nd string to it.
Stop the 5th fret of the 2nd string making note E and tune 1st string to it.
Check the 6th and 1st open strings together.

NOTES ON THE GUITAR IN 1st POSITION

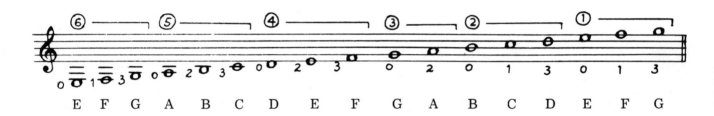

E   F   G   A   B   C   D   E   F   G   A   B   C   D   E   F   G

For the explanation of Musical Terms such as "bar", "beat", "syncopation", "accent", etc., see Chapter on "READING GUITAR MUSIC".

For the explanation of such terms pertaining to the Guitar as "Rest-stroke", "Free-stroke", "Barre" (BIII...), "½ — Barre" (½BIII...), "⅔ — Barre" (⅔BIII...), etc., see Chapter on "CLASSICAL GUITAR TECHNIQUE".

THE STRATA SYSTEM APPLIED TO CHORD DIAGRAMS

(A System that enables the non-reader to play solo arrangements).

There are many people who play the guitar quite well up to a certain standard, but who are very poor readers. This unfortunately includes many with a good ear and natural approach to music, many of whom may wish to play these solos. Fairly simple arrangements of present-day popular music seem to be scarce, perhaps because it is thought that there are not enough players whose reading enables them to take advantage of them.

Most of these, however, are familiar with the ordinary Chord-Diagram system, and can perhaps work out time-values (how quickly notes should follow one another) from written music if they know the song. The extension here of the diagram system should enable them to play the complete arrangement — melody and accompaniment — not simply the chord background. This process should therefore lead to a certain familiarity with notation and an understanding of the value and purpose behind a study of the Chapter *Reading Guitar Music*. This in turn should result in a level of reading ability which enables the player to continue with the solos beyond this stage.

THE DIAGRAM SYSTEM on which the STRATA SYSTEM is based is one that has always been used on printed copies of popular songs. Six vertical lines represent the strings, usually starting at the top from a horizontal double line representing the nut, then a few more horizontal lines for the first few frets.

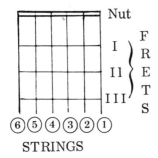

Black dots, or circles are placed on this grid — on the strings and just behind a fret, indicating whereabouts on the fingerboard the fingers are placed.

In the case of black dots, a figure indicating which finger is used is put at the top of the appropriate string just above the nut. O = open string, 1 = first finger, etc. If circles are used, the finger number is often placed inside the circle.

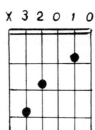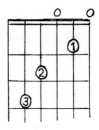

No indication, or a cross (X) on or above a string, means that this string is not allowed to sound.

Since this system is used only for strumming, or any other form of accompaniment, this is all that is necessary. How the player plays the chord with the right hand (strum across, bass-and-chord, or arpeggio), is up to him.

Let us now extend the system to indicate a definite style of accompaniment — say in $\frac{3}{4}$ — picking a bass-note with the thumb on the 1st beat, and picking a three-finger chord on beats 2 and 3. No left-hand fingers need to change throughout the bar, so the actual notes played can be indicated on one diagram, and we can use three separate rows of numbers above the diagram to indicate which strings, (and left-hand fingering), we want the right-hand to play, and in which sequence — one row for each beat — starting from the top.

If, instead of using a short bass note, we want it to sustain throughout the bar, we must indicate in some way that it still sounds while the other beats are being played.

For this purpose an asterisk (*) is used, and throughout each row in which it appears this finger is held down (and the note therefore sustained).

8

In order to avoid writing repeated rows unnecessarily, a figure in a bracket after a row
indicates the number of times it is played.

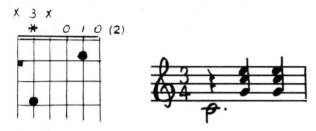

If (still in 3/4) we wish to play first the bass-note C
on string ⑤; next, the chord on the 2nd beat, and
then the Bass-note G on string ⑥, we write:

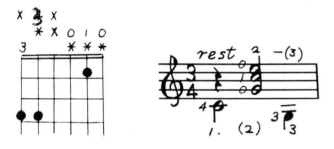

So far we've only used *one* chord in the section
covered by the diagram (in this case one bar). This
time let us suppose that the first two beats are on

C, but the last beat is Am (A minor); we could
then write it thus:

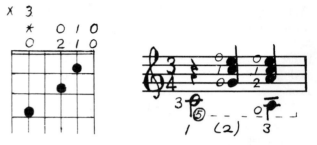

You will notice that two strings — ⑤ and ③ — are
each used in two different ways. On the first beat
string ⑤ is stopped at fret III with the 3rd finger
to play the note C. On the last beat it is played
open, (A).
String ③ is played *open* on the second beat (note
G) but on the *last* beat the 2nd finger plays A at
fret II.

*So you can see that one shouldn't just form the
chord without first looking at what the top row of
figures says.*

Going further, let us take a well known tune that
can be written satisfactorily in the ordinary diagram form: "God Save the Queen" or "My
Country 'Tis of Thee".

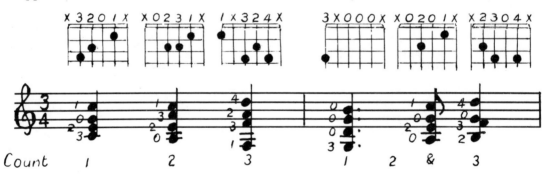

However, most arrangements of songs will not be
as simple as this, and far too many diagrams would
be needed — a new one every time a note or chord
changed — so, as before, it is necessary to be able
to pack more information into each diagram,
condensing the above, but still in such a way as to
be able to distinguish between each set of notes
played.

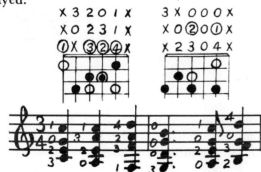

As you can see by looking at the above example, to
use dots of all the same type would require more
concentration and encourage confusion.

In the first bar we can use black dots and open
strings for the first chord. And, since the second
chord does not need a second dot to be placed on
any string, we can use any existing dots required,
plus open strings. The 3rd chord, however, intro-
duces extra fingerings, (on ② and ④), so if we use
circles to indicate the whole chord, and put circles
around the figures in the *row* that indicates the
fingering, it will stand out from the others.

The second bar I have worked out a little differ-
ently. Because in the first bar the second beat
involved no new notes except an open string, we
saved our circles for the radically different third

beat. But in general it will be found that, as in bar two, the *second* beat should have the circles, and the *third* beat may revert to dots.

Now if you correctly finger each row and pick the indicated strings with your right hand, (assuming you know how the time should go) you should be able to play thus far. If your ear tells you that something is wrong, check your reading of the above steps. However, should you feel unable to follow the timing of this or any of the solos in which the 'Strata System' is used, refer to the section *Reading Guitar Music.*

Perhaps at this stage a few points should be mentioned.

1. A number in a circle placed above the diagram means a new fingering, *not* a string-number as used in conjunction with staff-notation.
2. A cross (X) is used *not only* to mean that a string is not to be played by the right-hand, but also helps (especially in the top row) to space out and locate the strings used.
3. *No marking at all* above a string *also* means that it is not used.

So far we have only considered melodies that move in chords; we also need to show how single-note movement can be taken into account.

Let us use another well-known tune, 'Greensleeves':

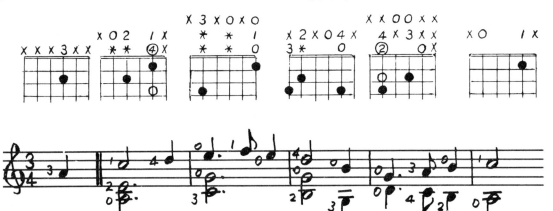

(The fingering in the 4th bar may seem a little different to some, but it is to save fingers jumping across strings and breaking up the 'flow' of the music).

Here is another way of arranging it, with a more placid flowing feeling:

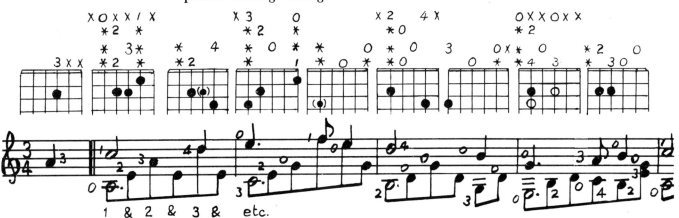

1 & 2 & 3 & etc.

This illustrates the use of this system in arpeggiated chord passages, as well as scale-wise movement in both parts (Bar4), but leads to a large number of rows of figures. This has been overcome by using more than one diagram to the bar. In $\frac{4}{4}$, one in each half of the bar would be the most common, but in $\frac{3}{4}$ it would tend to be 2 beats on one, one beat on the other — mathematically equal division would not make *musical* sense.

Asterisks over string ⑤ in the second diagram in each bar indicate that this string is sustained from the previous chord. Retain the finger on any note indicated by a dot in brackets:—

HIGHER POSITIONS

No difficulty should be found in reading this system in the higher positions if it is realised that the nut and intervening frets are not shown; the required position is indicated by a Roman numeral at the left of the diagram to show the basic fret at which to form the chord or phrase.

To illustrate this — and to sum up the other features — we will use the last two bars of *God Save the Queen* (also known as *My Country 'Tis of Thee*):

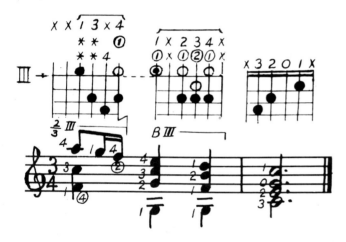

1. We see that there is no double line across the top of the first diagram, and that the phrase is based on the IIIrd position.

2. We finger (with the left hand) whichever *black dots* in the diagram are indicated in the *top row*.

3. We *sustain* two notes (marked *) during which:

4. We play, from Row 2, *a circle* (to distinguish from the black dot already played on that string).

5. Then, in row 3, a *black dot* on string ②, (the first time this string has been used),

6. A dotted line from fret III continues to the new diagram, indicating that we are still in position III.

7. We continue, playing the second diagram and see that a note on the 6th string is *common to both chords*, therefore it is played first with the dots, then with the circles.

8. There is also a horizontal bracket above the top row of fingerings. When this extends across the six strings — as it does in this case — it denotes a *full* Barre, but it may also extend across an appropriate number to indicate ½—Barre or ⅔—Barre.

9. We see by the double line across the last diagram that we are in the 1st or 'nut' position.

10. If we have timed the rows correctly we will have played the last two bars of "God Save the Queen".

THE FOOL ON THE HILL
(Tempo: moderately slow.)

The introduction and first four bars of the song are in Ist Position. For the first half of the fifth bar we move to position II (1st finger on F♯, at fret II on string ①), then back to Ist position until the last beat of the sixth bar. The seventh bar is in position III (1st finger on C – fret III, string ⑤). In the last half of this bar the 4th finger holds the A (fret V, string ①) while lifting the others and while playing the open B (string ②). It then slips back to position I for the following (8th) bar.

The last 2 beats of this bar will probably reveal a weakness inherent in most left-hands — the difficulty of stretching an adequate distance between the 2nd and 3rd fingers. As indicated here, the 2nd finger leaves the E on string ④ at the same time as the 3rd finger descends for the D on string ②. Although these are not sounded together some difficulty may be found; try, however to do it without moving the hand. The reason for fingering it this way (and not *4th* on D) is that the next bar requires a shift to position III with — among other things — the 3rd finger on the E on ②. The shift is made much simpler if the 3rd can slide up string ② and the other fingers form around it. (This principle of using a finger in this way to progress from chord to chord should be applied wherever possible).

One case where this technique cannot be applied is from the last beat of bar 6 into bar 7; and again at bar 14 into 15. Here there is no "link" finger between chords. (These, and other cases you may find for yourself, make good material for practice towards strength and independent control of the fingers).

Another typical chord-changing situation is from bar 4 (last beat) to bar 5. While playing the C on ② with the 1st finger, stretch the 2nd, 3rd, and 4th fingers towards the new chord-shape.

IMPORTANT: Remember always to relax the hand between one chord and the next; use your strength only to hold down each chord, not to fight your way *to* them. The best way to practise chord-changing is as follows:
1. Play a chord.
2. *Relax* from that shape.
3. Form the fingers *towards* the new shape.
4. Put fingers down *together.*

A piece should be fingered in such a way as to make it as easy as possible to play, without sacrificing musical considerations — particularly the smooth flow.

Although there can be cases where equally effective alternatives exist, I feel that the student would benefit by staying with the fingering as marked. In the early stages of learning a piece — in a rather disjointed and stop-go fashion — it is not always clear which way is best. Later, when the hand is able to maintain a more or less continuous state of motion, these things become apparent. Try to avoid fingering habits that can lead to a crisis-point in your playing; otherwise you will have to rid yourself of them later.

Bar 17 illustrates the mobility of the 1st finger, which holds the E♭, (I, ④) and later in the bar holds the C (III, ⑤) then back to the E♭, while the other fingers continue to hold the E♭ chord on the first three strings. *(During this, there should be absolutely no hand or wrist movement).*

In bar 19 we move up to position III for the F7 chord — held for only one beat since we have to move back to Ist position for the rest of the melody.

Prepare for the Barre on the 1st beat of bar 20 during the open string D of the previous bar.

Some may find the barres at the end difficult to maintain. Strength in this respect develops by *doing* them. Only use the muscles you have to; relax the rest (of the hand, arm, shoulder, etc) and do not allow yourself to strain.

Bars 10 and 14 contain ½–Barre — see end of chapter on 'Classical Guitar Technique'.

If in any difficulty with the crotchet triplets in bars 7 and 9 (♩♩♩), refer to the chapter "Reading Guitar Music".

THE FOOL ON THE HILL

JOHN LENNON and
PAUL McCARTNEY

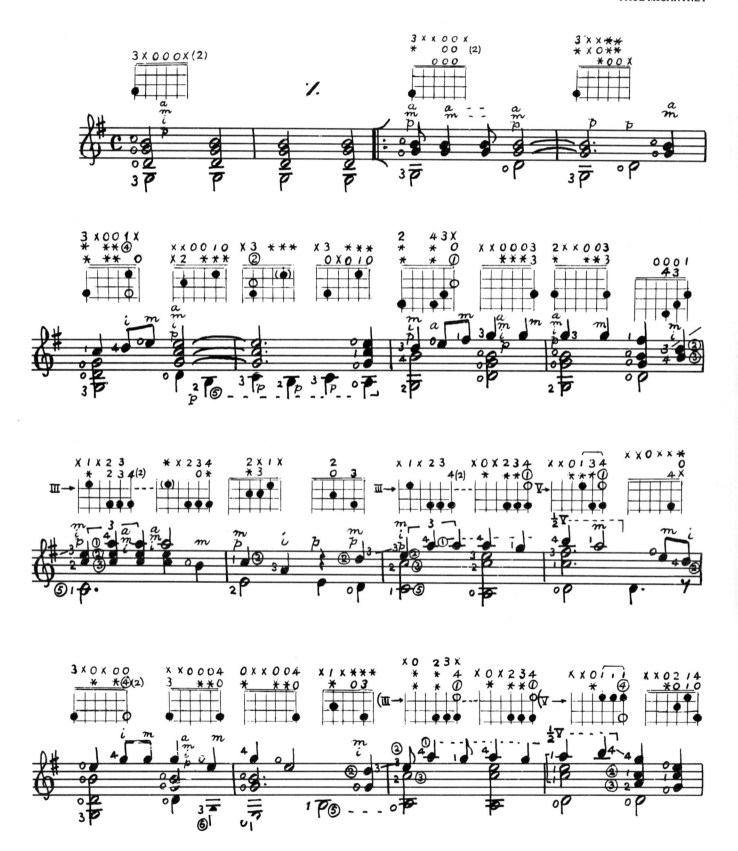

12

THE FOOL ON THE HILL

14

ALL TOGETHER NOW

JOHN LENNON and
PAUL McCARTNEY

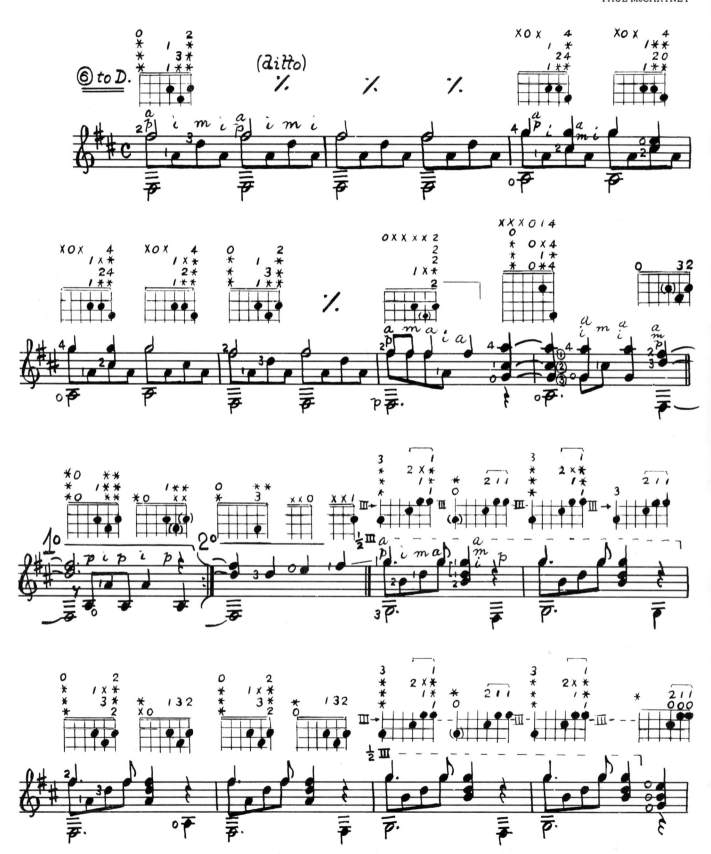

ALL TOGETHER NOW

ALL TOGETHER NOW
(Moderately Slow Tempo)

In this solo the sixth string is lowered a whole tone to D, (sounding an octave below the open ④.) This results in the note E — to which it is usually tuned — being now a fret II; and of course *all* notes on ⑥ will similarly have to be played two frets higher.

The Melody (above the arpeggio accompaniment) should be played *Rest-stroke* (See the chapter "Classical Guitar Technique").

Listen carefully to make sure that where melody-note and bass-note occur on the same beat, they sound *together*, (a rest-stroke simultaneously with *p* free-stroke).

The second section provides good practice for the ½ Barre, particularly if you prefer to finger the D chord in bars 3 and 4 of this section $\frac{1}{2}$, (½ II). (This of course may apply whenever this chord occurs).

Two examples of Syncopation occur: in bars 6, 7, and 8 of the first section, (where the accent normally falling on the 1st beat of the bar is — by the use of a tie — thrown on to the previous beat); and in bar 8 of the second section, (where the accents are made to fall *in between* beats). If there is any difficulty arising out of this, see the section on Syncopation in the chapter "READING GUITAR MUSIC".

Notice that the chord on the third beat of each bar in the second section should be fairly short, as indicated by the crotchet rest on the fourth beat.

FROM A WINDOW
Moderately Slow Tempo

Throughout this solo there is a strong rhythmic feel generated by the basic rhythm structure upon which the melody rests.

It combines the rhythm guitar part:

and that of the bass:

Together they form the basic Side-drum/Bass-drum pattern. You will therefore appreciate that you alone are playing the parts of several players, and the whole rhythmic interplay must be contained within the right hand. Start slowly; with this type

of rhythm you can go as slowly as you like and it should still sound alright.

The syncopation in the first few bars will tend to work itself out naturally if you *think* and *count* with an 8-Beat feel to each bar.

The syncopation in the 2nd Section is a little more complex, but continue to count in 8's; also consult *Reading Guitar Music* for hints on "doubling" the note-values as a means of getting the "feel".

Other things to watch: the position-changes in Bar 5, (remember to keep the thumb under the first finger and the wrist steady). Also, in Bar 5 of the 1st Section, relax on the chord-changes (see notes on *Fool On The Hill*). Once again, no wrist movement should occur.

The slur over the 2-quaver group (Bar 1, 3rd beat), means that the 1st finger (on F) snaps off to sound the open E (actually picking with the left hand). Make the *finger* do all the work — the *hand* does not move at all.

There is a rather quick change of position from the last chord of Bar 6 to the first chord of Bar 7, but this is made easier by the fact that the latter is the well-known 1st-position chord of C.

The main benefit derived from a thorough control of this arrangement will be the growing feeling of a separate, steady rhythmic function of the thumb — a feeling of being *independent* of the function of the fingers — so that it works "by itself", without conscious effort, allowing you to concentrate your attention on the melody.

I recommend the Right-hand fingering as marked; there can be a certain flexibility in such matters, but a tendency to develop any one-sidedness in technique must be avoided — such as the use of one particular finger consecutively (*i,i,i* . . .), or the failure to integrate *a* into the general system. It is largely a matter of leaving a finger in the best position to play a following note, thus helping string-location.

Most music should *sound* easy and natural, and therefore ease in playing will help greatly. *Remember always* to begin practising at *a tempo which is easy for you*; this will help to avoid building tension and insecurity into your playing. As with Left-hand fingering, the advantages of correctly planned Right-hand fingering become most apparent when the piece begins to "come together" and flow.

(Those using the *Strata System* will notice that Bars 9, 10, 11, 12, 13 and 14 are the same as the first six bars of the solo).

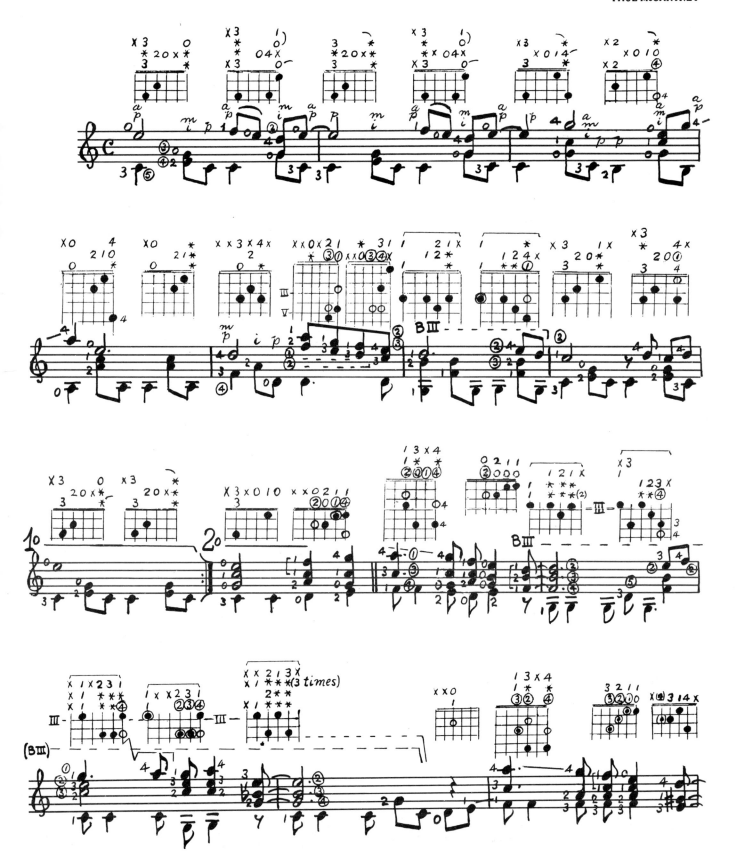

FROM A WINDOW

JOHN LENNON and
PAUL McCARTNEY

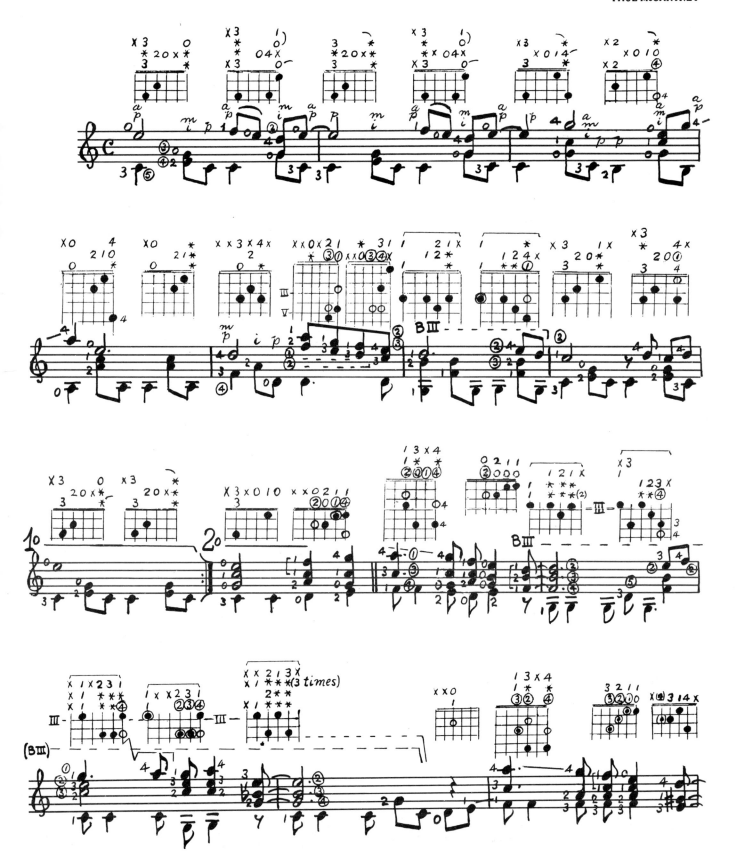

(3 times)

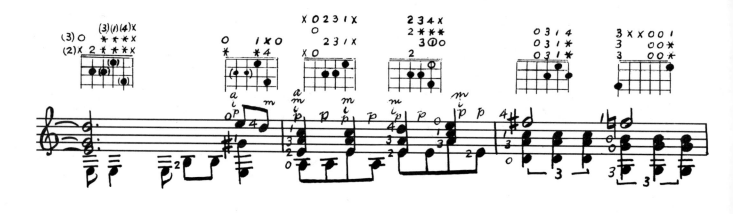

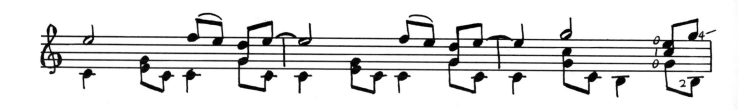

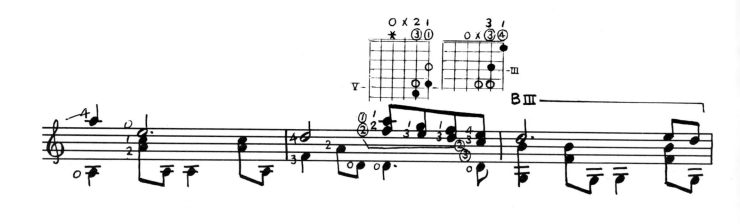

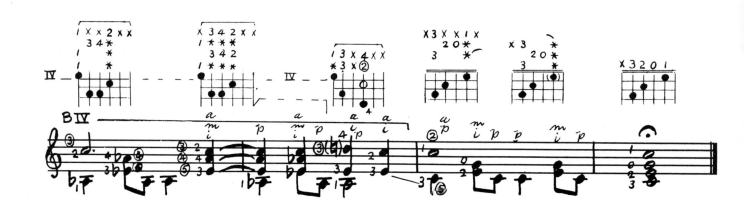

ALL MY LOVING

JOHN LENNON and
PAUL McCARTNEY

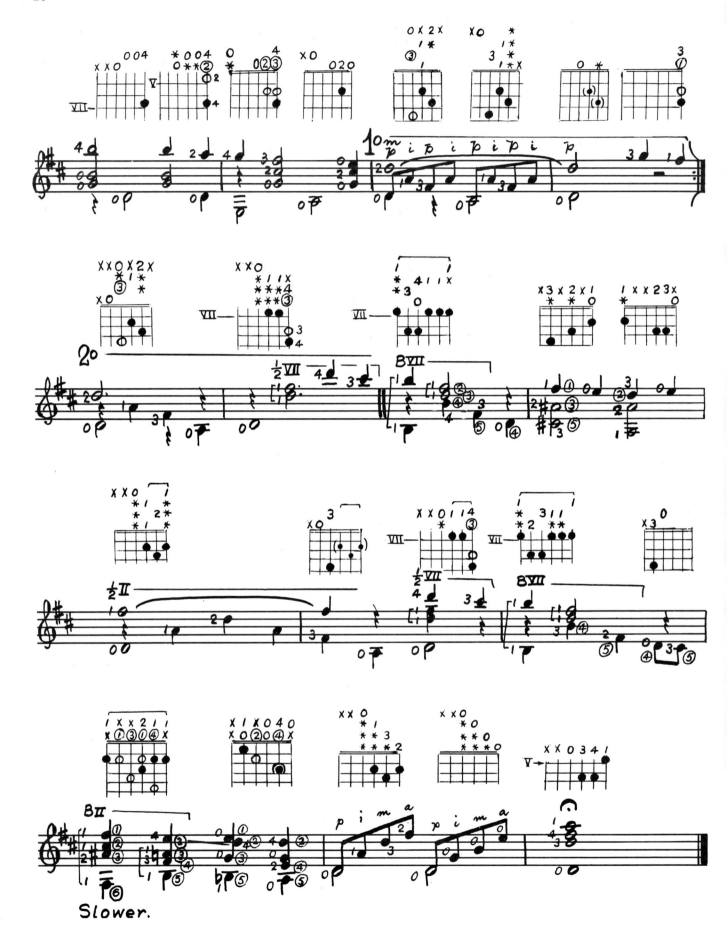

Slower.

ALL MY LOVING

Tempo: MM ♩=96; 8 Bars = 20 sec.
This arrangement is simple and straightforward as to time-structure; however we get farther away from the first position and improve our knowledge of the fingerboard. (The *Strata System* diagrams may be of help to those who are unsure in the higher positions).

All single melody-notes (those with stems upturned), or those beats involving only one finger and thumb together in the Right Hand should be played *rest-stroke*.

There is more use made of the block movement of small chord-shapes (e.g. the first three bars); open strings are employed to make changes of position more leisurely. (Bars 1 and 5 of the last section are instances of this — the open D helps in the change from BVII to BII).

Observe that in Bars 2 and 3 (of the 1st Section) the 4th finger remains on the string as marked: 4-4-4. This helps to stabilise the hand, but does not mean that one should hear a sliding effect (or *portamento*).

The 2nd finger is held down on E ④ throughout Bars 6 and 7 and part of 8 as indicated by the dotted line below the stave.

In Bars 11 to 12, care is needed in going from ½VII to BVII (½ Barre to full Barre), to ensure that the hand-position is correct and that therefore the wrist does not need to move.

In Bar 2 of Section 2 keep the 2nd finger held down throughout. After the 1st beat, the 1st finger can be moving across towards ⑥ while the next note (open E①) is sounding but the 3rd finger (on C,⑤) should be held as long as possible before moving to the D on②.

In Bar 5 the last note (C,⑤) is played with the 3rd finger, thus getting the hand in position for the BII in Bar 6. The tempo can slow down here, and the four chords should be practised until they melt smoothly one into the other. (In the change from the 2nd to the 3rd beat the 4th finger slides down②).

IF I FELL

Tempo: MM ♩=96; 4 Bars = 10 sec.
May be played in an easy flowing style at the above tempo, or *ad lib* — varying the tempo from time to time as you choose — a more "romantic" intrepretation.

There are more changes of position in this piece, but no difficulty should be experienced until perhaps the middle section, when it becomes mainly a problem of reading and relating to the fingerboard. If the diagrams are used to assist, make sure you are at the right fret — change position according to the Roman Numerals — and *first* look at the *black dots only;* then at the circles.

Notice also that sometimes a diagram relates to half a bar, three-quarters, or a whole bar. As usual, the melody should be picked out in *rest-stroke* wherever possible.

The 2nd finger slides up ③ from the last quaver before the double-bar into Bar 1 (A to B), while the 1st finger is moving across for the barre. Two fingers (2nd and 1st) move down their respective strings in Bar 2.

From the last beat of Bar 8 into the *2nd Ending* it is important that the 3rd finger should slide up ① from F♯ to A, thus making a rather awkward chord-change easier. In this (the first bar of the Second Section) the 1st finger is lifted off ③ on the 3rd beat to allow the open G to sound. The last two quavers (F♮ and G) are fingered by the 2nd and 4th fingers on ②, and the 2nd remains held down to form part of the next chord (in Bar 2).

Notice that the last chord in Bar 2 has an open string (②), while the other notes in the chord are played at Position X. This means that care must be taken so that the 2nd string is completely free to vibrate.

In bars 3, 4 and 5 the barre (BVIII) is held while considerable work is done by the other fingers. Something similar also happens on BIII four bars from the end.

IF I FELL

JOHN LENNON and
PAUL McCARTNEY

a little Slower

PLEASE PLEASE ME

JOHN LENNON and
PAUL McCARTNEY

PLEASE PLEASE ME

Moderately, with a smooth, even beat.
Mm. ♩ = 87, 4 Bars = 11 sec.

This piece is easy for those with an adequate ½ Barre technique, and good practice for those who have yet to achieve it.

The Strata System works well here and should greatly help those who need it. (Where no diagrams appear at various points in the 1st Section and Interlude, these bars are identical with some previous bars or portions thereof).

Make sure that the left hand position is correct, and that it doesn't move when changing to and from ½ or full Barre, also that there is no tendency for the hand to move when executing the snap in Bar 3 of the Chorus; only the operative 3rd. finger should move.

The syncopation in Bars 8 to 12 may trouble some, but they should try counting in quavers (1&2&3&4&), first becoming familiar with the top part (with upturned stems), then the bass (down-turned), then play both parts together. There is a little Barre work in Bars 10 and 11, and the hand will be in a good position for the not-so-usual chord of D in Bar 12. Whichever way the *right hand* picks the first 2 beats — whether a/p a/i/p, or a/p a/m/i, avoiding string ② creates a slight problem. However, it is most important that these chords are played *cleanly*, that neither *a* nor *p* accidentally touches ① or ④ during the playing of this bar, thereby either muting a string or causing a buzz. The open E at the end of the bar allows the hand time to move to the next chord.

At the end of the 2nd Time bar the use of 4th finger allows fingers 1 and 2 to move towards their positions for the next bar (the 1st bar of the middle section).

The Left-hand fingering for the last section is much the same as for the First, the most important difference being in the use of the ⅔ Barre in bars 1,3,5 and 7, instead of the ½ Barre as formerly. (This is, of course, so that the E (on④) may be included in the chord).

The usual device of arpeggio accompaniment is used in this chorus for variety, but the first section may be used here instead if preferred.

The.last note of Bar 12 is a *harmonic* — played by touching string ⑥ lightly at the 12th fret and raising the finger as soon as the harmonic sounds.

On taking the Sign the first section is not repeated — the Coda is taken after 14 bars. (The first bar of the Coda may also be used in this form in Bars 1 and 3 of the Introduction if preferred, also Bar 15 of the first section).

The piece should finish softly, and the dots over the notes in the last 2 bars mean that these notes are to be cut short, just after sounding. This is called *staccato*.

(For information on shortening or "damping" notes see instructions accompanying *Can't Buy Me Love* (No. 15).

BABY'S IN BLACK

Mm. ♩.=37, or 2 bars = 13 sec. Slow and relaxed.

In $\frac{12}{8}$ time each beat is split into three equal parts (see "Reading Guitar Music"). It can be considered similar in feel to $\frac{6}{8}$.

This arrangement is in the key of E; there are four sharps in the Key Signature so all F's, C's, G's and D's will be sharpened (except where altered to their "normal" pitch by a Natural sign (♮).

Only the first section can be covered by the Strata System, and even then some bass movement (such as that in bar 4) cannot be shown. However it should indicate to those with poor reading ability the exact location of the notes. The second section is based almost entirely upon the same chord-shapes as the first, but with more movement in the arpeggio style.

After the first two beats in Bar 1 very little hand-movement is required for the barre on II and, for the first two beats of Bar 2, the 3rd and 4th fingers merely move down two frets. The remainder of Bar 2 will test the left-hand position — indeed will be all the more difficult if the *guitar itself* is not correctly held. The necessarily cramped position of the fingers, together with the need for the 4th finger to move across from the last D♯ on ② to G♯ on ① with as little break in the music as possible, requires control. (Practice and perseverance with such passages help to improve one's playing).

On the last beat of Bar 3 the 3rd finger is raised just in time to pick the A and D♯ together.

In Bar 4 the Strata System indicates the upper and middle parts but not the right-hand arpeggio movement in the bass. At the end of this bar there are two open notes which simplify the movement to position VI in Bar 5. The fingers are already in position for the run of Sixths on the second beat.

Notice the change of fingering for the second of the three (C♯ –A); this is a *minor* sixth whereas the other two (D♮ –B and B–G♯) are *major* sixths. The hand should then be in a good position for the chord on the last two beats.

After playing the $\frac{6}{8}$ bar (only half as long as the others) the section is repeated, then there is a 2–bar interlude, the first bar of which is all done on BIV.

On the third beat of the following bar the movement is on string ②, and on the last beat the 4th finger first plays the A then comes back to play G♯.

The first six bars of the Second Section are — for the left hand — exactly the same as in the First Section, so that although the first two G♯ melody-notes appear as quavers (as do the other notes in the arpeggio) they actually sound through because the whole chord is held. The arpeggio (or broken-chord) figure is imposed upon the chord by the right hand so as to create movement and variety. (This also applies elsewhere throughout this Section). Observe the right-hand fingering and, if possible, use Rest-stroke on all melody notes. (See Chapter "Classical Guitar Technique").

Gradual slowing down of the tempo (called either *Rallentando* or *Ritardando*) may start at any point you feel appropriate (usually somewhere in the second-last bar). The last bar can be made slower still.

Note for those using the Strata System: in addition to dots and circles, squares are also used to help to distinguish between fingerings.

A line joining brackets between the 2nd and 3rd lines of music indicates that the last beats of both Bars 3 and 6 are identical.

BABY'S IN BLACK

JOHN LENNON and
PAUL McCARTNEY

AND I LOVE HER

JOHN LENNON and
PAUL McCARTNEY

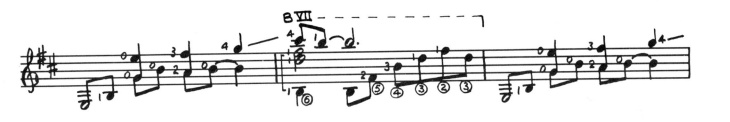

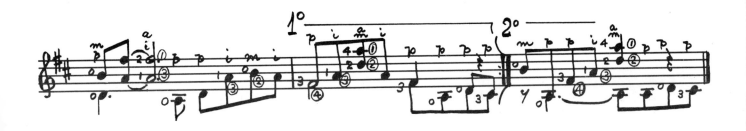

Slower

AND I LOVE HER

(Leisurely – about MM ♩= 75 or 4 bars = 13 secs. approx).

A "classical" style arrangement, employing more of the instrument's traditional forms. It should sound rather "rhapsodic" so keep it moving smoothly along; too strict a regard for the rhythm may make it sound a bit stiff.

The syncopation in bars 2, 4, 6, and 8 (not counting the Introduction) is given a fairly "classical" interpretation; rather strict. In the 7th bar observe that it is not possible to hold the bass note G as long as we would like; we hold it until the D sounds, than have to move up to fret X for the next melody note. (Notice the open 'D' at the end of the previous bar, which enables us to get back from VII to the 'G'). In the 3rd bar of the middle section we hold the barre on VII and move to the 2nd string for the last two melody notes, then come back down, placing the 4th finger at V on ①, and move the hand into the barre II position after striking the A. Then we apply a similar procedure with the 1st finger on B on ⑥, and the phrase as in bar 3, but broken up into triplet-groups. Practise to attain smooth and effortless shifting.

The B minor chord in bars 4 and 6 may be fingered in either of two ways:– on strings ⑤ and ④, $\frac{4}{3}$ could be used instead of $\frac{3}{2}$.

The last section is all broken up into triplet-groups and played as though in $\frac{12}{8}$. (Actually there is no practical difference between $\frac{12}{8}$ and $\frac{4}{4}$ broken up this way). Notice that the syncopation still occurs, but is fitted in exactly with the triplet feel. Don't be put off by the complex look of *stems up*, making crotchet triplets, and *stems down*, making quaver triplets – the whole thing just keeps flowing steadily on. But again, pick out the melody with *Rest-stroke*.

Most of this section is based on held chord-formations; the notes will ring through as long as the chord is held, and the effect will be not nearly as short as it may appear on paper.

In the third last bar, the 2nd finger must be lifted after two beats, the others still being held down firmly. This is no problem once strength and independence are achieved.

LET IT BE

Tempo: Fairly slow and smooth, about MM ♩= 68, 2 Bars = 7 sec.

This is a good study for the combination – in arpeggiated form – of *a* rest-stroke followed by *m* and *i* free-stroke; also for getting the left-hand changes clean and smooth so that no breaks occur and no notes are left out during change of chord-formation. The tempo should be kept steady throughout. Expression is obtained by increasing and diminishing the volume.

In the 2nd bar it is advisable to lift the 1st finger off the D♯ on the 3rd beat – in case the D♯ should ring on and clash with the E (open①) – then putting it down again on the last beat to begin the falling bass-progression which continues over the next two bars.

In bar 14, in order to preserve the timing of the original, the last beat employs a snap, keeping strictly to the timing of the group.

On the last beat of Bar 16 the hand moves back to Pos. I and the 3rd finger plays the F♯ on ①. This makes it easier (after having held the D♯ and F♯ as

long as possible) to position the 2nd finger on ② for the E (first note in Bar 17), and then immediately form the BIV. The changing-over of fingers –replacing the 3rd by the 4th on the C♯ (③) – on the 3rd beat may require a little work.

You may find it a good idea, for the first 3 beats in Bar 24, to put down the whole E Major formation at the beginning of the bar; not one finger after the other as and when called for.

This solo should not prove too difficult at the above tempo, but Bar 25 requires a good strong barre, and Bars 5, 7, 11, 17–18–19, 20, 24 and 25 may require some work. (Take advantage of open strings, etc., at change points).

The slowing-down effect in the second last bar will be enhanced by the change into $\frac{4}{4}$, (two notes per beat instead of three), then back to the very leisurely last $\frac{12}{8}$ bar.

Clarity of melody and smoothness of accompaniment are important; and again: do not "sacrifice" any notes to get changes in.

LET IT BE

JOHN LENNON and
PAUL McCARTNEY

BECAUSE

JOHN LENNON and
PAUL McCARTNEY

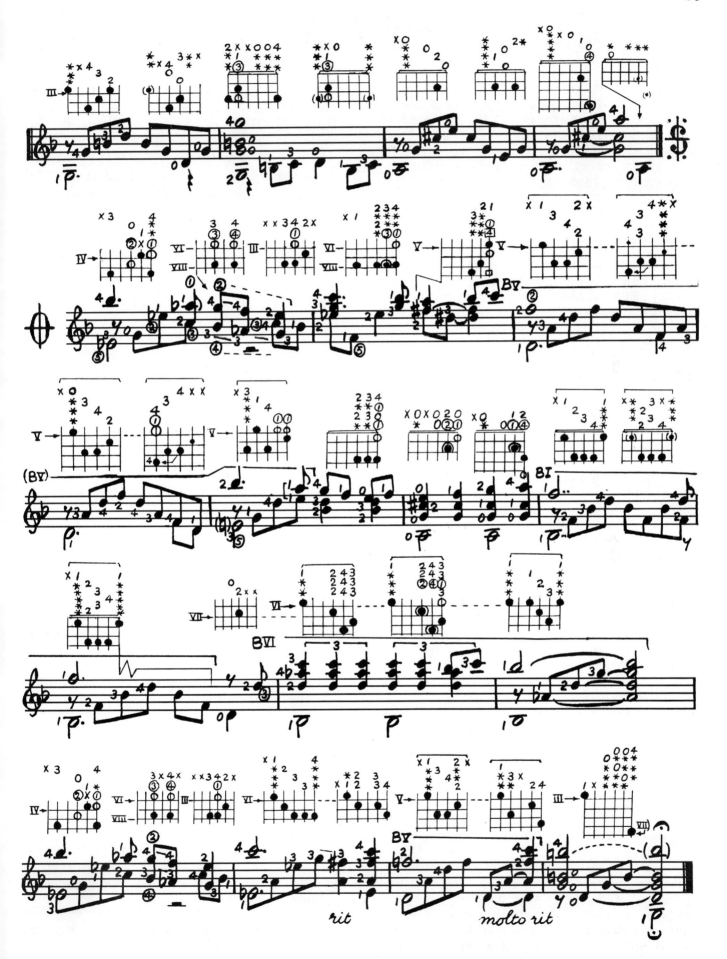

BECAUSE

Mm ♩ = 80, or 2 Bars = 6 sec.

The Introduction can be played *ponticello* to obtain a similar "colour" to the original version. This is done by simply picking the strings nearer the bridge — the closer to the bridge the more metallic the tone. In this position the fingers of the right hand tend to pick across the string at *right-angles,* instead of the normal "slicing" across in the direction of the right elbow.

The diagrams, combined with the marked right - hand fingering, should help those whose reading is poor — especially if they know the tune.

On the last beat of Bar 9 the 1st-position chord-formation can be released and the open G played, during which time the hand moves up the fingerboard, playing the following note (B♭) with the 3rd finger on ④. This gets us into position for the following bar.

Keep the 4th finger down throughout the first 3 bars of the Chorus.

At Bar 7 (marked "nat") the right hand should move back to its original position and a "natural" tone produced.

Bar 1 of the 1st ending is the same as Bar 9 of the Introduction, but this time we approach it from the 7th position and so it is more convenient to stay there. However, the last two quavers (G and B♭) are best played as in Bar 9. Practise for a smooth change in the last bar of the 1st. ending, bearing in mind that the 4th finger stays on ② and moves down a fret to F♯.

Repeat this Section and take the 1st ending. The bass melody in the last bar of the 2nd ending and in the 4-bar interlude should be brought out firmly. The Sign is then taken and the first 8 bars of the Chorus played again, after which we take the Coda sign.

In Bar 1 of the Coda the 1st finger has to move across from the E♭ on ② to A♭ on ①; try to make the change-over *without loss of time.* After the Sixth (C-A♭) on ① and ②, the following two (on the 3rd beat) are played on ④ and ② (at frets VIII and VI respectively). The B♭ on the last quaver in the bar may be fingered after the G-C-E♭ chord is sounded. In the next bar (2) follow the same procedure, play the $\frac{4}{3}$ chord at fret VIII before putting the 1st finger on F (⑤), VIII). There is just time to establish this as a bass-note and then the 1st finger must move to ① for the B♭ melody; the others (3rd and 1st) remaining until after this is struck. The 1st then moves down a fret and 2 and 3 change strings.

It is important that the 2nd should remain on ②, moving down one fret to the F♯ in Bar 3, at the same time forming BV. During bars 3 and 4 the 4th finger moves from ③ to ⑤, but this is quite leisurely owing to the note in between.

The hand is now in position for a fairly easy change into Bar 5, and the melody stays on ① for this and the next bar.

At the end of Bar 8, whilst the open D is sounding, the hand moves up and plays the last quaver (D) at fret VII on ③, *at the same time* forming BVI and the rather awkward chord in Bar 9. (Practise this until it is under control).

On the 2nd beat of Bar 12 (the third-last bar), the 3rd finger has to move as smoothly· as possible from ③ to ②, then back a fret on ②.

All fingers must change for the chord in the next bar, but the slowing down of the tempo makes this easier.

In the last bar, hold the B on ① if possible whilst playing the G on ⑥.

STEP INSIDE LOVE

(Tempo — 4 bars = 8 to 9 secs. mm. ♩ = 120 to 106. strict $\frac{8}{8}$ feel).

Continues the process of developing the thumb as the anchor to the whole rhythm structure. Looks more difficult than it really is, and some who could otherwise manage it may be put off by the problems of reading. I have therefore put chord diagrams at most of the change points. These do not cover all of the action (as they do in preceding solos) but one would expect a certain reading

ability from a student with sufficient technique to play it. So, if you need this help, use the experience to improve your reading. Even when you have memorised the solo, play it through occasionally while at the same time following the written part. It is not much use trying to get farther than this point unless one's reading is reasonably dependable.

The ½-barre on II may take place at the beginning of Bar 5, or 2 beats later.

STEP INSIDE LOVE

JOHN LENNON and
PAUL McCARTNEY

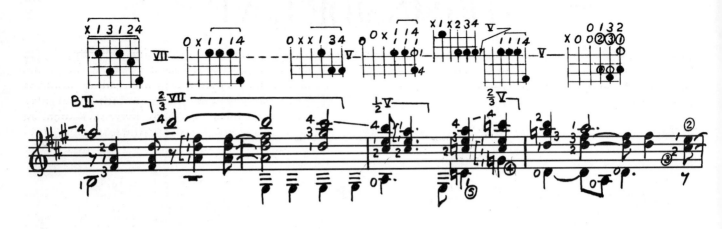

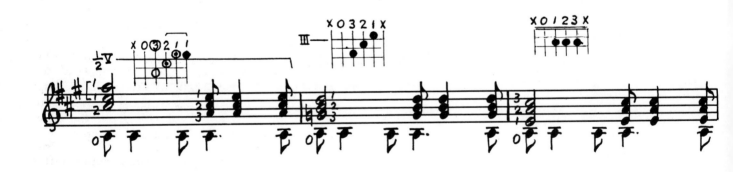

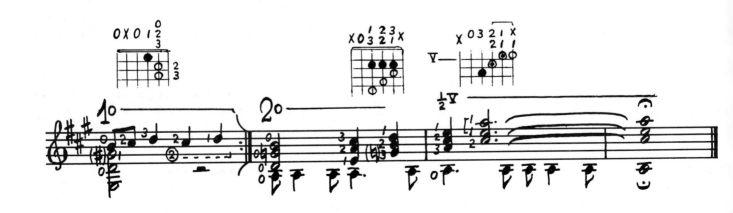

HEY JUDE

(The natural tempo is about MM ♩= 77, or 8 bars = 25 seconds, with a strong and even 8-quavers-to-the-bar feeling, but it may also be taken *ad lib*, if preferred).

The introduction starts at fret VII with fingers 3 and 4 on strings ③ and ② respectively. The 1st string remains open, and is picked as marked alternately in between the others in the order ③ ① ② ①, ③ ① ② ①, etc.

Although the right hand picking *p i p i* or *p m p m* would perhaps be easier, I have recommended *pipm* — *i* and *m* alternating on the 1st string. This is really to encourage players to get used to spreading the load equally between *i* and *m*, and not becoming centred on any particular finger.

Throughout the first two bars the 4th finger remains at fret VII on string ② while we descend on ③ a fret at a time.

In the last half of bar two, the 1st finger, having played C, extends a further fret to B. At bar three we begin a similar situation again at III on ② and ③, but finishing on the 'E' chord which starts the tune proper.

The first chord — the simple chord of A may be fingered as marked, or if you have a strongly developed habit of using 4/3/2, you may do so. I slightly prefer the former because of the F♯ at the end of the bar, also in the interests of versatility.

I mention this at length to make a point: in fingering the piece the aim is to make it as easy to play as possible, without sacrificing musical considerations — particularly the feeling of flowing smoothly.

In bar three, move to position II (1st finger on A, II, ③), the open D then allowing us to move up to position V to start the run of thirds — fingered so that the last one in the bar brings us into position for the first half of bar five.

In bar five, after the simple D chord, we do a quick shift to position VII for another run of thirds. This time they are syncopated instead of being written thus:

The second and third notes of the runs are anticipated, and this gives a "double tempo" feeling and a slight sense of urgency to the phrase.

Although to many these phrases come quite naturally (especially these days when one hears them so often), anyone who has reading problems may not know how it should go until he can play it, and vice versa. To help overcome such an impasse I often suggest rewriting the phrase in longer note-values and counting it out in a slower tempo:

(Count) 1   2   3   4   1 & (2) & (3) & 4

(Foot) 1   2   3   4   1   2   3   4

The bass note D in brackets is optional — I prefer it, but it may give trouble at first.

I also prefer bar ten to be treated as follows:

Again re-writing it:

1 (2) & 3 &(4)& 1   &(2)& 3 &(4)& 1 2 3 4

1 2 3 4   1 2 3   4   1 2 3 4

In bar 11 there is a ½ barre on II, then full barre II in bar 12, but raise the tip of the 1st finger a few notes later to allow open ⑤ to sound the A, while still holding the F♯ on ① a fraction longer, as written. All this repeats a few bars later.

After this, we have the recapitulation of the first section, but this time we take advantage of the long notes in the melody to ornament the bass part, giving it an independent life of its own. Here again, if in difficulty, try doubling out the time-values, also adding extra bar-lines if it helps.

In the bar before the last repeated section (after the first beat in position I), the 2nd finger moves up string ③ where we move across the strings, (a phrase based on the well-known V-position A chord, starting a fret below and moving the formation up, back, up etc in parallel, over an A bass, open ⑤).

The last four bars can be repeated and faded (or repeated and just finished at the end of the last bar) with or without slowing down.

Any difficult bits should be used as practice-material. Observe the cardinal rule of *slow* and careful practice for control. Do not frantically repeat, in the hope of gaining speed. Instead, you will only gain a tense, accident-prone style of playing.

HEY JUDE

JOHN LENNON and
PAUL McCARTNEY

42

WITH A LITTLE HELP
FROM MY FRIENDS

JOHN LENNON and
PAUL McCARTNEY

WITH A LITTLE HELP FROM MY FRIENDS

(Tempo: MM ♩= 96; 4 bars = 10 sec.)

This arrangement is the first of three which are in the Jazz idiom. Instead of each beat being divided into 2 equal notes (like a clock ticking),

the melody is composed of quaver-semiquaver groups:

This gives a characteristic bouncy feeling to the rhythm, and there is frequent syncopation which takes the form of *anticipation of the 1st and 3rd beats by tying the previous semiquaver to them.*

It is a good idea to accentuate the anticipated 1st and 3rd beats where this occurs throughout the piece.

When played with the correct interpretation it should sound happy and relaxed while the tempo is solid and firm. It's a good idea to tap your foot 4-to-the-bar *on the beat* (not phrasing with the melody), letting the melody go free. This will help in later solos in which the thumb has to play bass-notes *on the beat* while the melody follows its own independent line.

Not until the middle section does the latter occur; in fact the solo is so arranged that, for the most part, the player may get used to its bouncy style without the added complication of having to fit the bass notes into their *usual* places: on the beat.

In Bar 1 hold the bass-note C (on ⑤) throughout the bar. In bar 2 it is probably better to form the ½ BI on the 2nd beat rather than to wait until the 4th.

In Bar 4 accent the C on ② (just before the 3rd beat) and notice the rhythmic effect.

In bars 9, 11, and 13 there is some rapid work for the Right hand. Naturally "finger-style" technique cannot articulate this type of phrase with the smoothness of the plectrum; but since it is an essential part of the song one should *work to achieve a feeling of ease and control,* and not the "scuffling" effect that might perhaps otherwise result.

Special mention must be made of the last chord of Bar 2 of the middle section (D7♭5). It requires a complete shift of position and a complete re-grouping of the fingers and may take some time to get quickly and cleanly, but persistence and close attention to the order in which the fingers go down (especially that which you find best to put down *first*). Perhaps you may prefer to go straight to BIII for *this* chord instead of waiting till the next bar.

In the last half of Bar 4 of the middle section the low E (open ⑥) should be prevented from ringing into the next bar by the following means: when the R.H. thumb is in between ⑥ and ⑤ about to pick the A (open ⑤) in Bar 5, touch ⑥ with the flesh above the nail, thus stopping its vibration.

OB-LA-DI OB-LA-DA

(Tempo – 4 bars = 9 secs, m.m. ♩= 106)

Boogie-style walking bass, strongly marked and a very even ⅜ feel. Good practice for both hands in chordal playing; the R.H. fingering should be carefully studied. To give all your attention to the L.H. problems would be understandable but not satisfactory, as you would later discover. So start from the very beginning planning *both* hands together.

In Bar 6, try to sustain each note as long as possible, learning to overcome the inherent obstacles to a smooth two-way progression. Playing at a *very slow tempo* is the correct approach to the

whole piece; gradually achieving control.

A syncopated across-the-bar passage occurs in bars 9 to 16, the bass moving mainly with a strong 4-beat feel. In Bar 16 the BI is a good example of the importance of correct hand-position. The first finger should quite easily flick across, not disturbing the 2nd and 4th and without any movement of the hand. It is really all in the R.H. at Bar 17 – the L.H. just holds a series of not-too-difficult chords. (After going through it a few times you'll realise it's not so difficult).

Maintain a strong hold on the tempo in Bars 23 and 24; tapping your foot on the beat will help.

OB-LA-DI OB-LA-DA

JOHN LENNON and
PAUL McCARTNEY

CAN'T BUY ME LOVE

(Suggested tempo: MM ♩= 91, or 8 bars = 21 secs)

If the version of *With a Little Help From My Friends* (No. 13) — and other arrangements in this series which call for an *independent thumb* — are well under control, this one should present few further problems. Reading should cause no trouble, but, if necessary, the outline of the right-hand fingering may be perhaps more clearly seen by re-writing the piece as follows (this will also provide practice in the art of writing music):

In the introduction (which is used several times throughout as a device to tie the arrangement together) the beat should be a strong and even 1,2,3,4 and the quaver on the 4th beat of the first and third bars should not be played too short — just clearly separated from the following 1st beat of the next bar.

Throughout the whole piece there should be a feeling of four equally strong driving beats to the bar, and of course the melody — whether falling *on* the beat or *off* — must be emphasised. (It is presumed that the tunes in this series are quite well-known; there is no need to add to the clutter by placing accents over the melody-notes).

Of the tune proper, the 1st beat is clearly separated from the following one, therefore I have made a necessary change to a Barre after it is struck; and on the 2nd beat the chord is played with the same feeling, the formation being then taken away and the open B played. Interpret bars 5 and 7 in a similar fashion. The 9th bar should also be treated in like manner:

In effect, all of these on-the-beat melody-notes are played as broad quavers rather than as full crotchets, thereby giving the effect of greater accent without having to play them *louder*.

It may be timely here to point out that there are two ways of achieving this "detached" effect:

1. In cases where *all* the strings sounded are fingered by the Left Hand (either by separate fingers, barre, or a combination of both), relax the finger-formation sufficiently to allow the strings to rise just clear of the frets. This technique cannot apply to chords containing open strings except in cases where an open string can be touched by a L.H. finger during the relaxation process.
2. After striking the chord, replace the Right-hand finger-tips on the strings for an instant, before proceeding to the next note or chord. This method is effective in all situations, including those to which (1) may also apply.

For players who have complete control of this, or any guitar style requiring an "*independent thumb*", a further refinement may be added. The feeling of independence in the bass part is enhanced if it can be given a "pizzicato" sound similar to that of an acoustic bass, (double-bass):

After the thumb strikes each bass-note it then comes back to rest lightly upon the string, either with the flesh at the tip, but more often, (taking a bass-note on ⑥ as an example) coming back to rest between ⑤ and ⑥ so that ⑥ is *damped* by the flesh above the nail.

Some notes must, of course, be sustained longer than their written aspect would suggest. These will be melody-notes, such as the G♮ in the second half of Bar 1, which should be held down for the full duration of the following note B. This applies also to the first open E in bar 2, and so on; (We have already seen that in writing for the guitar one must compromise between the *strictly accurate* and the *expedient*).

Open strings are interposed in order to facilitate smooth changing from one chord or position to another. (once in bar 1; from the last beat of Bar 4 into Bar 5, and similarly into Bars 9, 10,11, etc.).

Remember that in all cases where open ② is used in this way it is played by m. This should then become quite automatic — requiring no thought — allowing the mind complete freedom to concentrate on the changes of position into Bars 5,9, and 11.

Some may prefer to use BV to play the A9th chord in the fifth bar, playing the bass-note A on ⑥ instead of open ⑤, (and also in Bar 11). In such cases one should perhaps do that which comes more easily, although *ideally* one should be able to do *either* with equal facility, since one does not always have a choice.

The last three bars of the piece are played on ½ II. The finger holds down strings ③, ④, and ⑤, leaving the open E (⑥) to be played in the last two bars. This, and the way the B13th chord is fingered, saves movement in the change of chord.

CAN'T BUY ME LOVE

JOHN LENNON and
PAUL McCARTNEY

HONEY PIE

JOHN LENNON and
PAUL McCARTNEY

HONEY PIE

There are certain similarities between this arrangement and the previous one; the same bouncy feeling of the dotted quavers followed by semi-quavers, the syncopated melody frequently falling *off the beat,* and the rhythmic effect of the independent thumb. However, whereas *Can't Buy Me Love* is written in the "blues" style, and should have a rather relentless four-beat feel, *Honey Pie* should go a little faster and have a smoother two-beat feel, more in the 'Twenties idiom. The slowest it should be taken is MM ♩= 113, or 8 bars = 17 sec.

The Introduction uses a well-known phrase from the period, which if recognised, should suggest the correct interpretation. It will be noticed that it contains short notes and rests, and the resultant "staccato" effect gives the phrase more urgency;

excitedly pushing along rather than smoothly "laying back" which would result if the notes were allowed to "spread" into one another.

However, since some players find *rests* more difficult to read than *note-values,* we may use note-values which fill the "spaces" between the notes; thus eliminating the rests, then tapping out the rhythm of the notes. This should (if your "timing" is correct) give you the exact feel of the phrase as played by the right hand. I strongly recommend this method of tapping out the "backbone" or *rhythmic structure* of any difficult phrase; it will help greatly to reach that very desirable stage where one sees the rhythmic structure of a phrase at a glance and can then attend to left-hand problems.

The left hand contributes to the desired effect by damping, a description of which is set out in the instructions accompanying the previous piece (No. 15).

These instructions should also be studied in-so-far-as they pertain to the special treatment required for the melody-notes.

In Bars 4, 12, 21, 22 and 28, a device is employed which is familiar to most players of "plectrum" guitar but may come as a surprise to "classical" players. The strokes between the notes of the chords are not to be confused with *portamento,* which is a sliding *transition in pitch* from one note into another. The effect of a true "slide" in the language of plectrum guitar playing is that of "hammering" one chord into another. In the fourth bar the first chord (⅔ IV) is struck and, pressing the formation down firmly, it slides quickly to fret V; the still-vibrating strings sounding the chord in the new position without picking again with the right hand. The movement is quite relaxed and rhythmical — the left hand

moves *at the instant the note should sound* — with a feeling of *playing it all.*

The third beat of Bar 6 is so fingered that it allows time to get the BIII on the last beat. In Bar 8, second beat, the 4th finger extends on string ③ to the D on fret VII, but the chord on the next beat (BIII) only requires it to extend to C at fret V.

The slide in Bar 12 is the same as that of Bar 4; but in the fifth bar of the middle section the 1st finger (BIII) does not move, while the 2nd and 3rd fingers slide together from fret IV to fret V. If this should be found to be too difficult, making a Barre at the beginning of the fifth bar may prove easier.

In the eighth (last) bar of the middle section the second chord should be damped by the lifting action of the left hand to make it short and crisp.

In the second last bar of the piece the ½-barre is across strings ②, ③, and ④.

TICKET TO RIDE

JOHN LENNON and
PAUL McCARTNEY

TICKET TO RIDE

Tune ⑥ to D. This tuning gives the arrangement quite a full sound, with a "busy" bass-part (plenty of work for the thumb). The Tempo should be at least MM ♩= 91; or 8 bars = 21 sec.

For those who haven't one already, this piece should help to develop a good ½ Barre, and the snaps in Bars 1 and 2 will put it to the test.

The need for an athletic 3rd finger will be apparent in Bars 1, 2 and 3; the strong hammer required in Bar 4 further emphasises this.

Fortunately there are only two different notes to be fingered on ⑥, (E, fret II; and G, fret V), and these cause no real difficulty in the "D" tuning.

In Bar 12 the five-note chord is played by the Right hand as shown; the thumb sweeps strings ⑤ and ④ in one action. Aim for exactly the same stress on this chord and the two preceding, a relaxed "falling" effect.

The shift to the last tied-over chord, (½V) in Bar 13, is made easier because of the similar shape of the previous chord.

A good hammer is required on 1st and 3rd fingers at the end of Bar 15.

In the middle section, the main notes of the melody need to be strongly accentuated, and the 2nd finger lifted off ③ and put down again without disturbing the other fingers.

NORWEGIAN WOOD

Tempo: First section, MM ♩= 80 or 4 bars = 9 sec
Second section MM ♩= 110 or 8 bars = 13 sec
Third section (in Harmonics), MM ♩= 80 or 4 bars = 9 sec

The above tempos should be close to the mark, and after practising each section separately, achieve a smooth transition from one to another. Naturally the tempo at the start will depend on the player — his optimum speed when playing tremolo. (In the development of tremolo some have found it helpful to practise the "flamenco" version — p,i,a,m,i, a 5-note group — after which they find the "classical" tremolo easier). The simplicity of the Left-hand part should make this section an ideal "TREMOLO STUDY".

The Second Section moves along considerably faster and should sound smooth and graceful in the upper (melody) part, while the lower part (played mainly with the thumb) should create the necessary rhythmic "drive". This is not so difficult to achieve in Bars 1,3,5 etc. (with only one long melody-note in each bar) but in Bars 2, 4, 6 etc., it is more complicated; firm control of the left-hand problems in this section will give to the bass-part some individual character, so that it does not merely fall mathematically on and between the melody-notes.

The latter half (about 18 bars before the Harmonics start) can be a little stronger — perhaps played closer to the bridge — then, 6 bars before the end, more gently; with the *Rall* over the last 2.

The Third Section goes back to the tempo of the first, or Tremolo section. For those who are uncertain about "artificial" harmonics let us take as an example the first note. The Left hand plays A (on ① at fret V); and in the Right hand, *i* rests lightly on the same string at the 19th fret *(always 12 frets above the L.H. note)*, and the string is picked by *a*. Lift *i* off the string *immediately* it sounds; and *a* is stretched as far from *i* as possible as this helps to produce a better harmonic.

NORWEGIAN WOOD

JOHN LENNON and
PAUL McCARTNEY

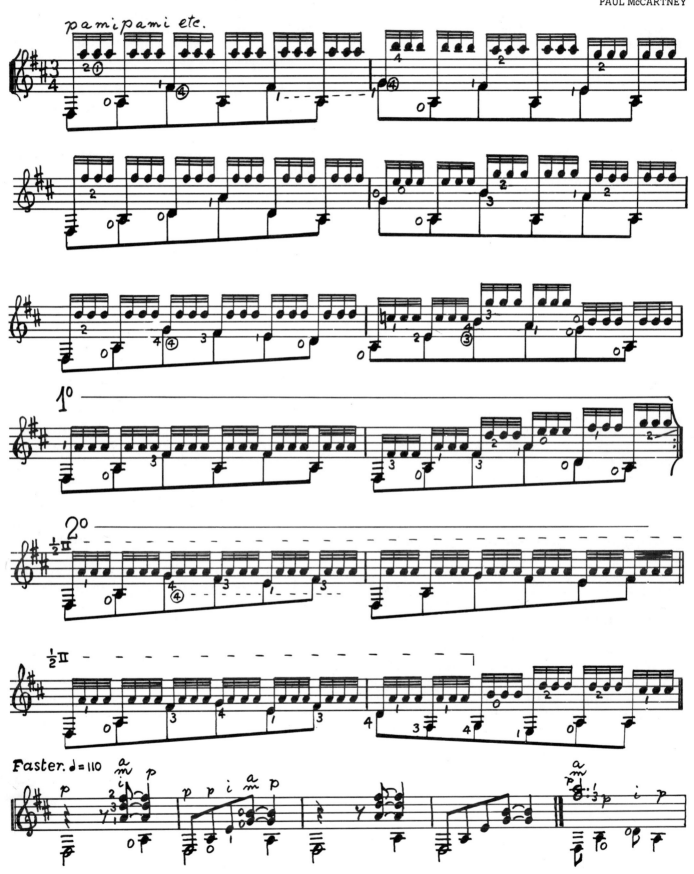

58

MICHELLE

(Moderately Slow, with expression)

Requires quite a thorough knowledge of the finger-board and the ability to read well.

Since there is not much "busy" movement, a strong left hand is required, with good tone-production and much *sostenuto*. This particularly applies to the Third section, 6 bars before going back to the Sign. Strong hammers and firm pressure of the left-hand fingers are required to make the notes ring out; otherwise you may consider it unnecessarily difficult — that you don't get enough out for the effort put in.

After the introduction, Bars 5 and 6 may be given either a very rhythmic interpretation, or smoothed out and played more blandly. (The same can apply to Bars 5 and 6 of the Second Section).

Bars 3 and 4 of Section 2 require a smooth change of position from VIII to VI, and somewhat of a stretch up ⑥.

The last Section may repeat twice or more, the last time slowing to a quiet finish.

Summing up, this arrangement requires left-hand strength, control, *correct hand position* (with "verticality" at the fingertips), and should amply illustrate the need for *the correct way of sitting and holding the guitar.*

MICHELLE

JOHN LENNON and
PAUL McCARTNEY

YESTERDAY

This solo is rather difficult, being somewhat fuller and more elaborate than a straightforward arrangement of the tune. However it will be found that the chord shapes around which most of the arrangement is constructed keep recurring, which makes memorising the Left-hand part easier without (I trust) any sacrifice of variety and interest.

The Bossa-Nova Section should have a rather strict 8-beat "feel"; don't be afraid of it sounding too stiff at first — it should soon settle into an easy, integrated bass-and-treble sound.

From Bar 15 of this section to its end, it has a "Double-tempo" feel. If it seems difficult to read — and therefore to "get the feel of" — try writing out these passages in doubled note-values:

Using this technique, the essential feeling of Bar 18 could be written as follows:

Mere *correct* and mechanical playing of these 6 bars will not suffice — you will have to get the feel of them and express a spirit of easy and natural animation.

In the last section the melody is mainly on ④, the chords on the last 2 beats of Bar 2 (in positions VI and VII) containing open strings.

The arrangement finishes softly with a chord in natural harmonics at the 12th fret.

YESTERDAY

JOHN LENNON and
PAUL McCARTNEY

Freely, ad lib.

Moderate Bossa Nova
Tempo   mm. ♩ = 92.

READING GUITAR MUSIC
(RUDIMENTS OF MUSIC)

It is a great advantage to be able to read music, indeed without this ability progress beyond a very simple level is impossible. Musical notation is not at all as complicated as it may first appear; it has very few symbols and their functions are easily understood.

Music (also called "staff-notation"), is written on a 'staff' or 'stave' of five lines, between which there are four spaces.

The vertical position of a note — on a line (the line passing through it), or in a space between two lines, or below or above the stave — indicates its pitch. That is to say how 'low' or how 'high' it sounds, and where it can be played on the guitar.

Whenever music is written for the guitar, the sign:

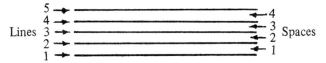

is placed at the beginning of every stave. This sign is known as the G or Treble Clef, and the curl in the middle of the clef ends on the second line of the stave, giving the name 'G' to the note on that line.

All other notes follow up or down, in alphabetical order, using the first seven letters:

To identify notes quickly they are divided into two clear groups — those on the lines:

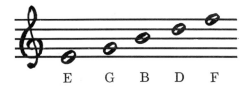

and those in the spaces:

To accommodate additional notes above and below the stave, short lines termed leger lines are used, on or between which the notes are placed — continuing the alphabetic sequence:

The difference in pitch between any two notes is called an *interval*, and the smallest interval we have in music is called a *Semitone*. Therefore the guitar is fretted in semitones.

The piano keyboard also is divided into semitones.

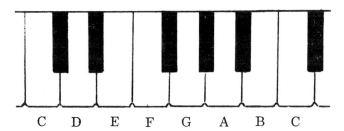

The white notes played consecutively from C to C constitute a major scale, (Doh, Re, Me, Fa, Soh, La, Te, Doh). Doh is in this case C, and the scale is termed C Major. (Each note recurs 8 notes, or an octave, higher).

From this it will be seen that the Major Scale is not composed entirely of equal steps. Between five pairs of adjacent white notes — C and D, D and E, F and G, G and A, A and B — there is a black note. Now, since the piano is tuned in semitones, there must be *two semitones* — or one whole *tone* — between these pairs of notes, but only *one semitone between B and C, and E and F.*

Regarding the black notes, the one that lies midway between C and D is a semitone *above C*, and is called C sharp (C♯); and because it is also a semitone *below D*, it is also called D flat (D♭). The fact that a note can have *two names* has very little significance regarding what we *hear*, since on the guitar, both C♯ and D♭ are found at the same fret and therefore sound the same, and this of course also applies to D♯ and E♭, F♯ and G♭, G♯ and A♭. However, as will be seen later, this dual identity is very useful in the writing — and reading — of music.

KEY SIGNATURE

In order to understand what is meant by "key", it is important to realize that a major scale may be built on any note – called the *Tonic,* or *key-note.*

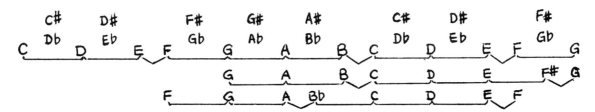

Because every major scale must *sound* like a major scale, ie, have its *tone* and *semitone* steps in the right order, those built on any other note but C will introduce either *flattened* or *sharpened* notes. If a major scale is constructed on each of the following notes – G, D, A, E, B, F♯, C♯ and F, B♭, E♭, A♭, D♭, G♭, C♭ – those in the first group will contain an increasing number of sharps, while those in the 2nd group ('flat' keys) will contain an increasing number of flats.

Since a scale may start on any note – and most songs are mainly based on the notes in a major scale – it follows that a song can be in *any* key, to suit a low, medium or high voice, or for ease of playing.

If it is in the key of G, chords associated with G will be used and the melody will be composed mainly of notes in the G major scale, ending normally on the note G.

F♯ will therefore tend to be used instead of F, and to avoid writing the ♯ against every F in the piece, a sharp sign (♯) is put on the F line at the beginning of the song, after the clef:

This is called the Key Signature, and indicates that for every F seen

F♯ is played:

But if, as sometimes happens, an actual F is called for, a natural sign is put (♮) against it, and it is called F natural (F♮).

Any sign which *temporarily* alters the pitch of a note, whether ♯, ♭ or ♮, is called an *'accidental'* and applies every time that this note occurs *in that bar:*

Thereafter it reverts to its normal pitch as governed by the key signature. (Obviously the more sharps and flats there are in the key, the more convenient the device of a key signature becomes).

FINDING NOTES ON THE GUITAR

It has been seen that the piano has its notes laid out in one long row (in linear sequence), one key only for each note and always in the same place. On the guitar, however, a series of steps is taken along one string, then along the next string for a few steps, and so on. Starting from the lowest note and staying in the 1st position (remaining within the span of the hand at the 'nut') the equivalent of the 'white' notes would be:

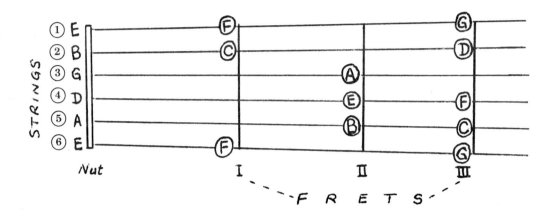

Starting on the lowest note (E, open ⑥) F is on its 1st fret, G (a whole tone up) is on the 3rd fret, the next tone A is the open ⑤ then B, C, D (open ④) and so on. Or, to indicate this in notation:

showing the written note, the string on which it can be played (①, ②, etc) and the finger which can play it (1, 2, 3, 4,). Since it is normal to use a finger to a fret — 1st finger behind 1st fret, 2nd finger behind IInd fret, and so on — in this instance the finger number is also the fret number; but of course this only applies to the 1st position.

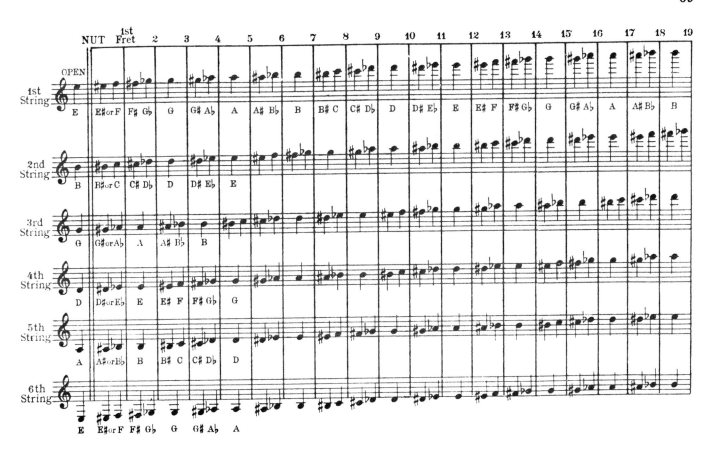

The Fingerboard Chart may be used to refer to, but it is not necessary to memorize by rote the position of every note; rather let it grow out of reading and playing experience. However, it is essential to learn immediately to recognize the notes on the stave, and to remember the open strings and where these are on the stave.

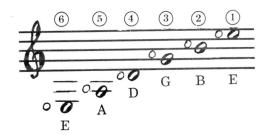

All notes from E (open ⑥) to G♯, (fourth fret on the 1st string) may be played in the Ist position, and any given note may be located by finding the nearest open-string note below it and counting up by semitones — one fret for a semitone — until it is reached.
Eg, the note D will be
on the ② or B string.
The Ist fret is C,
IInd fret C♯ (or D♭), IIIrd fret D.

Or again, to find G♯:   The
nearest *open* note *below* is E (①)
and we count up: E O, F I, F♯ II
G III, G♯ IV.   G♯ is on string ①, IVth fret.

TIME

This aspect of music — the Rhythmic component — is written along the horizontal dimension, and it will be seen that vertical lines are drawn through the stave. These are called BAR—LINES and divide it into sections called BARS. These sections are of equal length, ie., they each contain the same number of beats.

If we consider a person walking down a road and whistling a tune, the rhythm of the tune will almost certainly be directly related to the tramp, tramp of his feet — in other words, the tune would go to a left-right, left-right — or 1–2, 1–2, rhythm. To write this time down we would divide the stave into BARS, each containing two BEATS. (Let us say the tune was 'Baa-baa Black Sheep')

BAA	BAA	BLACK	SHEEP	HAVE	YOU	AN—Y	WOOL..
LEFT	RIGHT	L.	R.	L.	R.	L.	R.
1.	2.	1.	2.	1.	2.	1.	2.

In each of the first two bars there is one syllable — or melody-note — on each beat, but in the third bar each beat is halved — split into two syllables or notes, and in the fourth bar the word 'wool' takes up the whole bar (2 beats). Therefore notes of three different lengths must be used to indicate the exact time each syllable should take.

RELATIVE TIME-VALUE OF NOTES AND RESTS

The relative time value (or duration) of notes depends on their shape, without reference to their position on the stave. This should be carefully memorized.

A Semibreve (Whole note)	White note
2 Minims (Half notes)	White notes with stems
4 Crotchets (Quarter notes)	Black notes with stems
8 Quavers (Eighth notes)	Black notes with single hooks
16 Semiquavers (Sixteenth notes)	Black notes with double hooks

The Demisemiquaver (♬) and the Semidemisemiquaver (♬) are notes of still shorter value.

When two or more quavers, or semi-quavers, are written consecutively their hooks are joined together to simplify reading. They are always grouped to conform to the time-signature.

The following is a Table of Rests, (periods of silence) and each is equal in duration to the note of the same name.

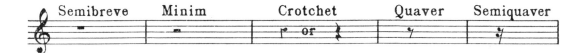

Semibreve	Minim	Crotchet	Quaver	Semiquaver

A dot placed after a note or rest indicates that its duration must be prolonged by one half.

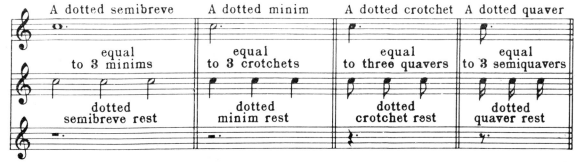

A dotted semibreve	A dotted minim	A dotted crotchet	A dotted quaver
equal to 3 minims	equal to 3 crotchets	equal to three quavers	equal to 3 semiquavers
dotted semibreve rest	dotted minim rest	dotted crotchet rest	dotted quaver rest

Two dots placed after a note or rest indicate that its duration must be prolonged by three-fourths. A double-dotted minim, for example, is equal to

The note commonly used as a unit of time — to indicate one Beat — is the Crotchet, or Quarter-note.

Baa   Baa   Black   Sheep   have   you   an - y   wool?

In the above tune we have, in each bar two of these notes (or other notes adding up to the same value), and it is therefore said to be in $\frac{2}{4}$ Time. To indicate this the sign '$\frac{2}{4}$' — called the Time-Signature — is placed at the beginning immediately after the Key Signature.

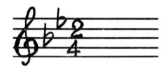

A TIE is a short curved line placed over, or under, two or more notes of the same pitch. They are then to be played as one longer note — equal in duration to the sum of the 'tied' notes.

ACCENT

There are three degrees of accent: Strong, Medium and Weak. The word "banjo" has a strong accent on the first syllable and a medium accent on the second, while the word "guitar" has a weak accent on the first syllable and a strong accent on the second. The word "mandolin" has three syllables, the first pronounced with a strong accent, the second with a weak accent, and the third with a medium accent.

There is nothing in the writing of these three words, or any other English words, to show how they should be accented. With music, however, it is different. The note on the first beat of a bar, or measure, is played with a strong accent. In common time, six-eight time, or any other time divisible in equal halves, the second half will commence with a medium accent.

The way in which notes are grouped together is also an indication of accent. All groups of notes, with the exception of those immediately following a dotted note, should have the first note played with an accent. Of course if such a note happens to begin a bar, it will have a strong accent, or if it begins the second half of a bar it will require a medium accent.

Special accent is also indicated by the sign $>$.

In the following examples, the initial letters of the words "Strong", "Medium" and "Weak" indicate the required degree of accent.

Notice how the words "banjo", "mandolin" and "guitar" can have their accents accurately indicated by means of musical notation.

Ban - jo   Man-do-lin   Gui -tar

S   M   S   W   M   W   S

It will be seen that accent in music is self-explanatory. If the player studies the foregoing rules and remarks he will more readily understand any music he reads at sight and consequently, get the right sense of a tune without having to rely on first hearing it played by another performer.

The rhythmic structure of a melody is determined by the disposition of its accents and the way in which they form into regular groups — or bars. In $\frac{2}{4}$:

S   M   S   M

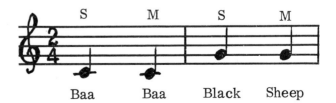

Baa   Baa   Black   Sheep

A melody such as *Rock-a-bye, Baby* has a recurring "Strong — weak — weak" feeling, having three beats to each bar. Such a melody is therefore said to be in ¾. (Three-Four).

In ⁶⁄₈ time, each bar contains six quavers, but they fall into two groups of three:

It is important to distinguish between ¾ and ⁶⁄₈; the first should be played as two groups of three, and the latter as three groups of two.

COMMON TIME

Most ballads are written in ⁴⁄₄ or Common Time, the disposition of accents for each bar being Strong, weak, Medium, weak (S, W, M, W,).

COUNTING TIME

The ability to read music at sight depends to a great extent on the player's grasp of TIME. Naturally, few people can sight-read well enough to give any sort of performance — usually it is a succession of small exploratory operations — but the time-structure should be the part that causes least concern, (as distinct from finding the *notes* on the instrument).

It is essential therefore to learn to *feel* the rhythmic structure of bars or musical phrases — in the beginning it may be necessary to learn to *count out* the various notes of a bar or phrase, keeping in strict time by tapping the beats with the foot.

Count and beat 1, 2 ,1, 2 for $\frac{2}{4}$
Count and beat 1, 2, 3, 1, 2, 3, for $\frac{3}{4}$

Count and beat 1, 2, 3, 4, 1, 2, 3, 4, for $\frac{4}{4}$ (C)

When quavers (eighth-notes) occur, the count for that beat can be one-and, two-and, etc, in *even* time, the foot keeping the main beat. To take a well known example:

Practise the following combinations of minims, crotchets and quavers:

Apply the same procedure to $\frac{3}{4}$:

Sometimes semiquavers (sixteenth-notes) occur, especially in $\frac{2}{4}$, and here one should not need to count out syllables for each note, but instead to

become able to play at sight a group of four notes in the time of one beat:

Also groups such as:

It is necessary to learn the feel of groups such as:

as soon as possible, and to learn to play them automatically to a simple beat or count (1 – 2, etc). If it helps to understand them they can be considered as:

played twice as fast: taking the smallest note as a unit and seeing the group as the sum of the fractions (1) ¾ + ¼ or (2) ¼ + ½ + ¼.

⁶⁄₈ metre, if slow enough, can be counted 1 – 2 – 3, 4 – 5 – 6; or 1 – 2 – 3, 2 – 2 – 3. If fast, (as it often is): 1 and–a 2 and–a; *all being equal.*

TRIPLETS

Each of the various types of Rhythm tends to maintain its consistency: beats in ²⁄₄ and ⁴⁄₄ tend to subdivide into groups containing 2, 4, 8, or 16 notes. But sometimes it is felt desirable, when a beat contains 3 notes, that they receive equal value

and equal emphasis. Any note can be divided in this way:

QUAVER TRIPLETS (three quavers in the time of one crotchet) are perhaps the most commonly met with, and if one understands ⁶⁄₈ time should cause little difficulty, since the effect is similar (disregarding the difference in the way in which each is written).

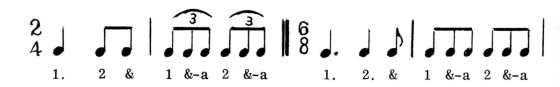

However, be sure to observe the difference between the two types of rhythm – in the ²⁄₄ example the quavers in the first bar are *not* equal in length, (½ + ½), to those in the second bar, (⅓ + ⅓ + ⅓).

CROTCHET TRIPLETS IN ⁴⁄₄ TIME

These occur frequently in popular music. They are somewhat more difficult to 'feel' since the tempo is slower and therefore the feeling of three-in-the-time-of-two is more pronounced – three notes

across two beats is more difficult to feel than three in the time of one. However it is unlikely in guitar music that a triplet group is to be played against two notes in another part (as in Bar 1. of the example:) but rather (as in Bar 2), three against one.

Nevertheless one should start, not too slowly at first, to beat 1 – 2 – 3 – 4; 1 – 2 – 3 – 4 with the foot until the rhythm is established, then to try singing da-da-da, da-da-da; *evenly* across each bar of four beats.

Another approach sometimes used is to beat 1, 2, 3, 4 with the foot, and sing

gradually *increasing* the values of the first and last quavers in each group at the expense of the middle (tied) pair, ending up with two equal triplet-groups.

SYNCOPATION

European music maintained a rather bland rhythmic structure, concentrating on the development of the more "civilized" aspects of melody, harmony, tone-colour etc, whereas other parts of the world have contributed rhythms of great vitality, variety, and subtlety. Many of these have been incorporated into current popular music, and so it is necessary here to take the first steps

towards understanding some of the reading difficulties syncopation involves.

Musical expression depends to a great extent upon the proper use of accent; and if we "break up" the time or transfer accents to unusual positions, we produce a syncopated effect. One of the simplest ways of bringing this about is by using the *tie*, (explained earlier in this chapter), in such a way as to shift the accent from the strong first beat of the bar back onto the beat before it, (the weak last beat of the previous bar).

Because of the tie there is no attack on the first beat of bar 2; instead we feel it to be on the previous beat — hence the re-distribution of accents as shown in the example above. To make it more pronounced, when one is used to the feel of this phrase, one naturally tends to "lean on" or accent this beat.

A well-known example of this is in "All Together Now" — which I have transposed into the key of A for easier playing:

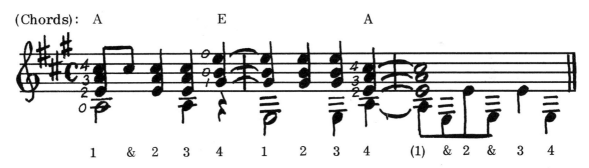

Notice that in the 2nd bar the Bass-note E still falls in its usual place (on the strong first beat), but when the melody-line *again* anticipates the 1st beat of Bar 3, the bass part goes with it also, taking up the rhythm again with a small featured solo or "fill".

Practise this until you can make it feel relaxed and natural — it is of little value if you have to continue to concentrate hard, or have to count, to get it right. Later on, syncopation becomes so complex that unless you get to know and *feel* them as familiar rhythmic forms everything will sound strained and uneasy.

A milder form of syncopation, (involving this time the *Medium* accent), occurs within the bar of $\frac{4}{4}$ by

— in effect — tying the 2nd (weak) accent to the 3rd medium:

I say "in effect" because it is usually written:

I say "in effect" because it is usually written:

A feeling for the above phrase will lead to an easier understanding of the next example, in which either, or both, the 2nd (weak) and the 4th (weak) accents are displaced:

1 & (2) & 3 4 | 1 2 3 & (4) & | 1 & (2) & 3 & (4) & | 1 2 3 4

This is written:

1 & (2) & 3 4 | 1 2 3 & 4 & | 1 & 2 & 3 & 4 & | 1 2 3 4

(This last phrase was used to acquire a feeling for the crotchet triplet-groups dealt with earlier, gradually lengthening the quavers, correspondingly shortening the crotchets, and finally making them all equal).

It is a practice among musicians, when there is a need for the leader or conductor to explain the interpretation of a phrase, to use sounds such as

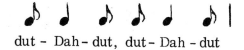

dut - Dah - dut, dut - Dah - dut

rather than counting:

1 & & 2 & &

since in many syncopated phrases the beat is *felt* rather than actually *played* by the "front line".

This is particularly useful when further displacement of accent tends to increase the feeling of urgency, agitation or excitement. The phrase then sounds as though it has its own separate and independent life upon a foundation of the "mentally" on-going beat — with or without the tapping in strict time of the foot.

Naturally this process can continue across bar-lines:

Dah Dah dut dut dut Dah___ Dah dut Dah Dah___

•anticipating the strong 1st beat, not by a crotchet or whole beat but by a quaver. An example of this is found at the start of *From a Window*.

Play only the melody-line for a start, beating your foot 4 to the bar (and if you like) counting:

(Count)   1 2   3   & 4   &   1 2 3   & 4   &   1   2 3 4   &   1   2 3 4

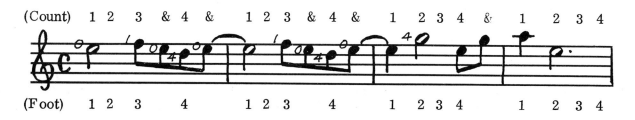

(Foot)   1 2   3   4   1 2 3   4   1   2 3 4   1   2 3 4

Count all of these as before and get them to feel quite natural, noticing that, if properly felt, instead of destroying the beat they make it felt all the

more strongly by implication. As an exercise, see if you can sound out (by tapping or other means) the following:-

Syncopation in 'Bouncy' Rhythm

The syncopation we've just dealt with only involves 'even' quavers, as if the time were mathematically divided into equal units, eg., a clock ticking, where each tick (in the above examples) would equal a quaver.

Most 'pop' music of latter years uses this structure (probably following 'bossa-nova', which arose out of a fusion of samba rhythms and jazz). However, the early 'rock and roll' or 'rhythm and blues' used rhythms similar to Jazz, Shuffle, or Boogie, and some derived directly from Ragtime and Blues guitar. A study of this latter would be by far the most effective way of achieving an easy familiarity with what follows; but, for the present, some of the main points can be dealt with.

The difference between a jazz or 'bouncy' feel and that which we formerly dealt with lies in the interpretation of the way a beat (crotchet or ¼ note) breaks up. In this case it breaks up into 2 unequal time-values which are written as a dotted quaver followed by a semi-quaver, or three-quarters of the beat taken up by the first note, the remaining quarter by the last note. The actual interpretation, however, is closer to ⅔+⅓. One must learn (if indeed one *has* to learn) to feel this instinctively — the interpretation is apt to lie between the two, according to taste and context. All that remains to be said is that syncopation in this style follows broadly the same lines as before, the main difference being that phrases involving groups of quavers are written:

with perhaps a little extra accent on the semiquaver:

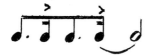

Groups such as

are similar to the other style ("even" quavers) but sound smooth and relaxed rather than 'mechanically' precise.

PARTS OR VOICES

In guitar music two or more parts are often played together, and it is often impractical to write everything *exactly* as it sounds, (a simple and obvious example being that of arpeggiated chords being written as a succession of short notes, whereas the first notes are still ringing while the last one is being played). However, we do our best to make the written music correspond with the way it should sound. This is particularly important where one part (usually the melody) needs to be made to "stand out," from the accompaniment.

Sometimes this is easy to do:
Fool On The Hill

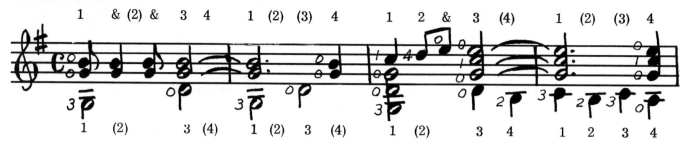

It clearly divides itself into two lines, and each is seen to add up to the right amount of beats in the bar. (The simple expedient of playing each in turn – first the part with stems up-turned, then that with stems down – will illustrate this). The melody is usually in the highest voice (and this in itself helps it to predominate) but occasionally it is in

the bass, and care must be taken to ensure that it is strongly emphasized.

Where more than two lines occur the same principle applies; we must still see clearly where each part comes in the bar.
If I Fell

Whereas the top part has the stems up and the bottom part has the stems down, the middle part has to be written – either up or down – in a way that most clearly separates it from the others. (If it lies near the top of the stave, farther from the bass than from the melody, it is best to turn the stems down, and vice versa).

Not all bars in any piece necessarily follow one rule. In the above example, for the first bar, and for three-quarters of the second bar, three lines are clearly visible. On the last beat of the second bar,

the upper melody-note E, joins the accompaniment, $C\sharp$ G on the same stem: the clearest way of showing it. Bar three appears to be in two parts but the minims (½-notes) on the first of each quaver-group, although treated as if they were in fact written as a group of quavers, indicate their importance as bass-notes.

Examples of using the direction of stems and also use of the tie to indicate musical values, (what to stress, what to sustain, etc.):
And I Love Her – as written:–

As actually played by the right hand:

REPEAT SIGNS

A Double-bar in music is equivalent to a full stop and denotes the end of a complete part or section. The double-bar is indicated by two thick upright lines through the stave.

When dots are added before a double-bar, the music from the previous dotted double-bar is intended to be repeated.

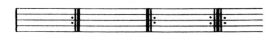

In cases of hand-written manuscript, brackets are often added:

When the Figures 1 and 2 (or "1st time" and "2nd time") are placed under lines at the double bars, the piece should be played first to the double bar but when repeated the bar (or bars) marked 1 are omitted and the bar (or bars) marked 2 played instead.

Example:

"D.C". or "Da Capo" placed at the end of a piece (or section) indicates that we are to go back and play *from the beginning.*

"D.C. al Fine" at the end of the music indicates that after having gone back to the beginning, we are to finish at a point in the music marked "Fine", which is its natural ending.

A CODA is a short section added to a piece for a more effective ending. "D.C. al CODA" (or "D.C. al ⊕") indicates that we are to go back to the beginning, play until we reach a sign ⊕, or "TO CODA", then go straight to the CODA (marked "CODA" or ⊕).

DAL SEGNO

"D.S.", "Dal Segno" or 𝄋 placed at or near the end of the piece, means that we are required, on reaching this point, to go back to a place (usually *near* the beginning) also marked 𝄋 If our instruction is *"D.S. al Fine"* we then finish at the place marked "Fine". If it reads *"D.S. al CODA"*, upon reaching the sign ⊕ (or "TO CODA") we then play the Coda.

CLASSICAL GUITAR TECHNIQUE

"Technique is, after all, only a means to an end". This statement has been made many times, the implication often being that natural ability finds its own way of doing things, and that there is no *right* or *wrong* way. However, without the means, the end is unattainable, and while it is true that many become perhaps a little too obsessed with technique to the neglect of other aspects, nevertheless a feeling of command, of ease and control is essential to good *musical* performance.

The obvious improvement in instrumental technique in recent years is due to a greater awareness of — and more intensive study of — the physical factors involved. In the case of instruments with a longer period of constant development, such as the piano, the string family, etc., it seems to be well-established that the way the human body and the instrument join in producing music allows of little variation from *a few simple basic rules, from which all else follows.* This principle is particularly applicable to the guitar.

WHAT IS SO "SPECIAL" ABOUT CLASSICAL TECHNIQUE

Since this body of technique has been developed to solve *all* of the musical problems that one is ever likely to encounter, one can learn *all* about *every* aspect of the instrument and not be limited to any one small area. All "folk" idioms become quite easy to handle, and one can put more into the instrumental side, as well as being able to play "solo".

SITTING AND HOLDING THE GUITAR

The most obvious difference between the "classical" way of playing and all others is the manner in which the guitar is held. It is of the utmost importance that it should be held correctly right from the beginning, since only in this way can the hands possibly assume their correct positions and — especially in the case of the Right Hand — for the fingers to learn to move in the best way.

Of course when one feels confident of one's basic technique more casual positions may be used on informal occasions, especially when no great demands are made on one's technique. It will also be found that standing with the guitar supported by a strap over the shoulder approximates quite closely to the 'classical' position. However, in more demanding circumstances there is *only one possible position, otherwise either or both hands are handicapped,* resulting in an insecure technique and the inability to do all that one would wish with ease and assurance.

1. Sit with a straight back on an ordinary chair with no arms; well forward so that the guitar does not bump against its edge.

2. Place the left foot *flat* on a footstool which is placed a few inches in front of the left leg of the chair. The footstool should be high enough to bring the left knee slightly above the hip. The lower part of the leg is maintained perpendicular to the floor — it does not lean to either side.

3. Place the guitar on the left thigh in such a way that its soundboard is perpendicular, (not tilted, with its lower edge stuck out so that you can look down into the sound-hole); it fits *snugly* over the left thigh with no space between, and as close to the body as possible. The centre of the peg-head should be on a level with your left shoulder.

4. The Right leg is placed out at such an angle that the guitar rests firmly against the inside of the thigh, and is thereby prevented from slipping down.

5. Lean slightly forward, and allow the back of the guitar to rest against the chest — square across, the peg-head neither poking out to your left front, nor around behind your left shoulder.

6. The Right Forearm — just below the elbow — rests *firmly* on the top edge, directly above the bridge.

7. Be quite relaxed — there should be no twists or tensions in any part of the body.

The guitar is now held securely at four points: left thigh, right thigh, chest, and right arm. *This leaves the left hand completely free for its playing functions.*

THE RIGHT HAND POSITION

1. With hand and wrist relaxed allow the right arm to hang naturally by the side. The wrist is *straight,* i.e., no angles; angles mean tension.

2. Retaining the straight wrist, lift the arm over and rest the forearm on the edge of the guitar. (The position of the forearm is described in 6. of "Sitting and holding the guitar").

3. The wrist is arched just high enough to enable the fingers to move freely under the hand without any movement of the hand itself.

If the forearm is positioned correctly the fingertips will rest on strings ①, ②, and ③ just behind the edge of the sound-hole.

5. Thumb and fingers are positioned in such a way that the thumb *never* at any time moves in *behind* the index finger and under the hand. The curve of the fingers and stretch of the thumb — each in opposite directions — ensure that the tip-joint of the thumb extends *past* the index finger.

6. Looking down on the hand, the fingers should move under its shape or "shadow", and the hand should be inclined — slightly lower on the thumb-side — so that the nails (particularly those of *i* and *m*) strike the strings not in the centre of the tips, but somewhat towards the upper corner of the nail. (This *also* assists in the correct relative positioning of thumb and fingers).

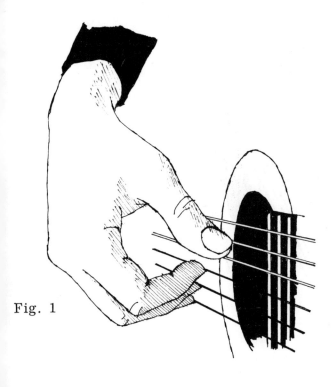

Fig. 1

7. It is preferable that the base joint of the thumb should stand out, the thumb not being absolutely straight; (see Fig. 1.). This gives the thumb greater flexibility and power. However, if you find this too difficult play with a straight thumb.

The matter of vital importance is that from this position the hand must be able to perform and interchange all of its normal functions without any adjustment.

4: The whole hand — including the fingers — should be well curved, (the longer fingers more curved), so that they are in effect of equal length when in contact with the strings. No finger must feel the need to stretch in order to reach the strings, particularly the *a* finger.

THE MOVEMENT OF THE FINGERS

I. FREE—STROKE

(a) All movement is from the main knuckle at the base of the finger. The finger – *maintaining its bent shape* – moves in underneath the hand, along a line in the direction of the elbow.

(b) The tip-joint – which is *always* relaxed – "flops" or flexes as it strikes the string. If the adjacent string is accidentally brushed the hand position should be adjusted; usually by curving it a little more over the strings, perhaps by moving the forearm and raising the wrist.

Any attempt to solve the problem by picking *up from*, instead of *down across* the string, will result in great sacrifice of control and tone-quality.

(c) An important objective is that the fingers should feel as though they *know* the position of the strings in all circumstances.

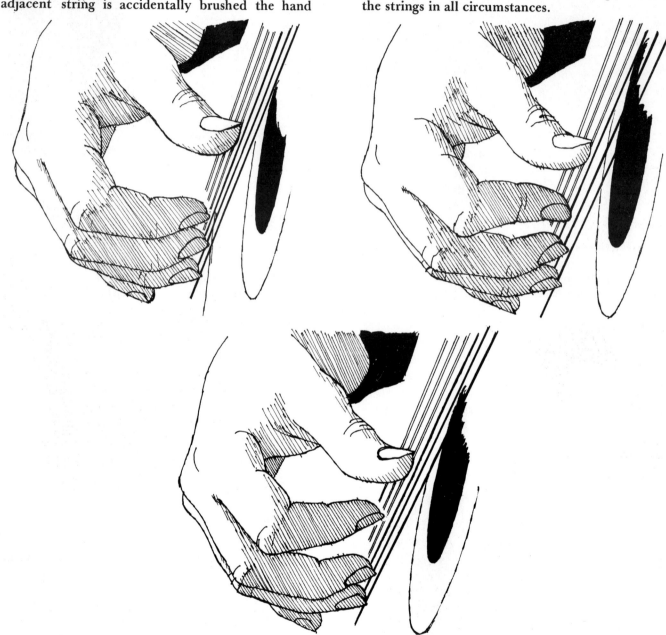

THE THUMB

The movement of the thumb is in opposition to that of the fingers. The *whole* thumb moves from the joint down at the wrist, and the tip joint does not flex at all. It should sweep across the string in a straight line towards the index finger, *not* in a circular motion.

POINTS TO REMEMBER:

1. The arm must be relaxed from *shoulder to finger-tip*.
2. The hand should remain quite still, a frame from which only the fingers move.
3. The action should be short; all movement – fore and aft – kept to a minimum.
4. Work at all times to develop the strength and independence of the fingers.

PICKING CHORDS

As emphasised before, the hand position remains the same. The movement of thumb and fingers is the same as for Free-stroke, the main difficulty at first being that of synchronising the movement of thumb and fingers. Each grouping of *fingers* moves together as a unit. Great care must be taken to ensure that no "plucking" action occurs — that *the hand does not bounce.* All movement is limited to the "snapping" action of fingers and thumb sweeping towards each other. *The hand must not be allowed to twist.* (The action of playing chords illustrates very clearly the relative movements of fingers and thumb: if these are allowed to stay together after having played a chord, *p* and *i* form a cross, the thumb at its tip-joint coming to rest a little above the tip-joint of the index finger).

Practise picking open strings in various combinations — *im, ma, ia, ima, pi, pm, pim, pma, pia, pima.*

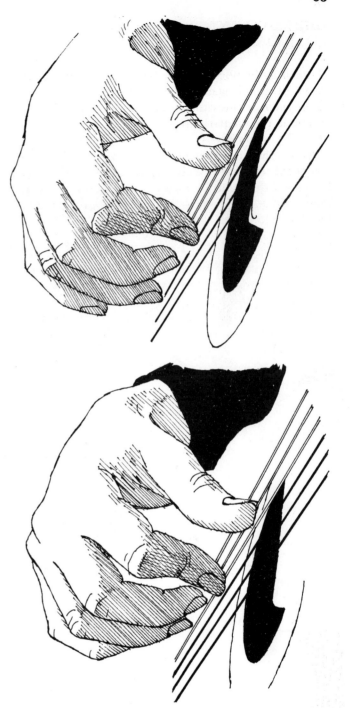

THE MOVEMENT OF THE FINGERS.

II: REST STROKE

This is a very valuable aspect of Right-hand Technique whereby a noticeably stronger tone is produced. It is of particular advantage in single-note and scale-passage playing, allowing the melodic line to be emphasised; and, applied to the thumb, bass-solo passages. It is possible either with one finger at a time, or with any one finger in combination with the thumb; or else with *i* and *a* together on non-adjacent strings.

In arpeggio playing it is only practicable on one of the fingers of the combination, (usually that on the higher string) and is not possible at all in chord playing. But without its dynamic force our playing would tend to sound somewhat dull and featureless; which would be a great pity, since it is not so difficult to acquire this technique.

1. With the hand in the same position as for "Free-stroke", the finger moves from the main joint at its base, and retains its bent shape.

2. The tip, (behind the nail), is forced down as though *through* the string: at one point only, *not sliding along the string.* The tip-joint, being *completely limp,* gives way *inwards* (towards the hand) and the string springs free.

3. The finger now comes to rest against the next adjacent string.

    N.B. Whereas in Free-stroke the direction of finger-movement is along a line towards the right elbow, in Rest-stroke the finger tends to move slightly sideways and more nearly at a right-angle across the line of the string, towards the centre of the player's chest.

Although many employ this stroke without the tip-joint bending, it is with some loss of control; but more importantly, a sacrifice in tone-quality. Whereas with flexing tips the tone is full and round, with stiff tips it is rather hard and "naily"; tight fingers — tight sound.

RIGHT-HAND MOVEMENT DURING SCALE-PASSAGES

There is only one occasion in general playing on which the Right Hand actually moves. This is when playing across the strings in single-note or scalewise passages, (particularly from treble to bass, or vice versa). It is obviously not possible, for example, to play a scale from string ① across to string ⑥ by moving the fingers only; they must be carried across by the hand in such a way that the normal relationship of fingers to hand – indeed the hand-position itself – is undisturbed.

The only way this can be achieved is to see that *the whole framework moves;* the forearm, pivoting from the elbow, moving across through a short arc and carrying the hand with its active fingers. If the arc starts on string ① it will finish on string ⑥ at a point a little further up towards the end of the fingerboard.

(The wrist may have to bend slightly as the hand nears string ⑥.)

If in playing a descending passage from ① to ⑥ the

hand were to move *back* across the strings *in the direction of the right elbow,* either the wrist would have to be raised or the forearm slid back on the guitar edge to adjust to this movement. This would then have to be followed by an immediate recovery of position and the likelihood of a breakdown. (The same of course applies, in the reverse procedure, to ascending passages).

Those who have read this section carefully will perhaps realise that the fundamental principle underlying this approach is to discover hand-positions from which *every* kind of operation can be executed under precisely similar conditions. Also that the various components (fingers, etc,) are given the conditions under which can be developed *independence and strength,* which lead to *control,* which leads to *speed.*

This principle applies equally to both hands.

THE LEFT HAND POSITION

1. Sitting and holding the guitar correctly, allow the Left Hand to hang down by your side, completely relaxed.
2. Turn the arm so that the palm faces to the front.
3. Without moving the upper arm, (only bending at the elbow), lift the forearm until the hand touches the edge of the fingerboard at the junction of the fingers with the palm. The joints at the base of the fingers should be about level with the edge, and the hand will be a few frets below the 12th fret.
4. Allow the thumb to extend across under the neck, (*under* the first finger).
5. Curve the fingers over until they press down on the third string. The tips of the fingers should descend at 90° to the fingerboard, *and the string should make a mark along the middle of the fingertip.*

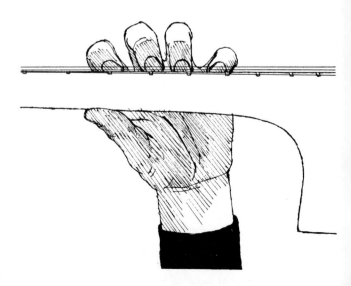

6. The bent fingers will fan out, being well-separated at their middle joints; the 1st inclining towards the peg-head, the 4th (little finger) with a pronounced inclination the other way (towards the bridge). The tendons down the back of the hand are therefore quite straight. (Studying the various aspects of the hands by practising before a mirror can be of great value in the formative stages).

7. With the hand in this position, the fleshy inside last joint of the thumb (the only part of it that touches the neck) should be just past the centre of the neck.

8. From the large finger segment, down the back of the hand and past the wrist, everything should be in a straight line; with no sunken-in knuckles or "kinked-out" wrist.

9. The back of the hand will be at right-angles (90°) to the fingerboard *surface*. This will be found to be, overall, the most comfortable position for the Left Hand; it is also the main reason for holding the guitar as we do.

10. Allowing the thumb — which is never more than just resting lightly against the neck — to slide across, move the hand away from the edge of the fingerboard and press the fingers down on string ①. The hand must still be close to the edge, always within ½" (12 mm), the fingers bending up a little more and the tips maintaining their "verticality", (falling 90° onto the fingerboard).

11. The knuckles at the base of the fingers must *never* fall below the edge of the fingerboard, (especially that of the 1st finger). Thus one always has access to the bass strings by extending the fingers — not moving the hand, (except the small movement against or away from the fingerboard edge).

12. Keeping the *whole assembly* from elbow to fingertips in exactly the same relationship, and only moving the upper arm at the shoulder, move the hand down to the First Position (first fret, next to the Nut). The forearm should — as

near as possible, depending upon one's physique — maintain its angle of approx. 90° to the guitar neck. If the elbow is kept close to the body — the forearm forming an acute angle with the neck — the joints at the base of the fingers will drastically change their relationship to the fingerboard edge; that of the 1st sinking below, those of the 3rd and 4th being somewhat above.

If you allow this to happen it then follows that your technique changes according to the position up or down the fingerboard — an unnecessary and often fatal complication.

THE BARRE. (BII, BVII, etc., also MC2, MC7, etc.)

This is a function that the 1st finger performs by virtue of its ability to hold down any number of strings simultaneously, greatly increasing the scope of the guitar.

Without changing the hand-position, extend the 1st finger across the strings, just behind and parallel to the fret, the tip of the finger *just* protruding beyond the sixth string.

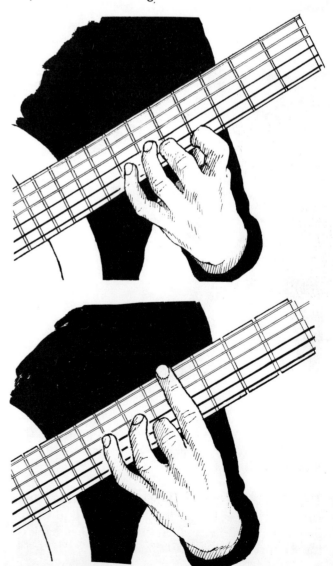

Although in some positions — notably the first — the wrist may tend to stick out a little, in general the ideal situation obtains: the 1st finger can flick across and back without disturbing either the position of the hand or that of the other fingers. *In no circumstances must the elbow need to swing backwards and forwards during this process.*

When *playing chords* do not allow the fingers to clump together or lean against each other. The knuckles should be clearly separated at all times; even in tight situations where the fingertips push in close together. Only by observing these principles will the player attain the required strength and independent control of each finger.

THE HALF-BARRE. (½II, ½VII, etc.)

The tip of the 1st finger presses three adjacent strings firmly down onto the fingerboard. The tip-joint sinks in, and the middle segment of the finger rises sharply, the middle joint remaining high above the fingerboard. The finger is not quite parallel to the fret, being angled back a little.

There is no apparent change of hand-position; the base of the fingers should still be level with the edge of the fingerboard.

The ultimate test is to duplicate a situation often encountered; with the hand in correct position, first form a full Barre, then a ½ Barre, then back to full Barre; *all without hand movement.*

THE TWO—THIRDS BARRE. (⅔I, ⅔VII, etc.)

The 1st finger covers four adjacent strings, otherwise the   Barre is in all respects similar to the Full Barre.

Printed in England by WEST CENTRAL PRINTING CO. LTD., London W1P 1

Music Sales' list includes music played and sung by every artist of note

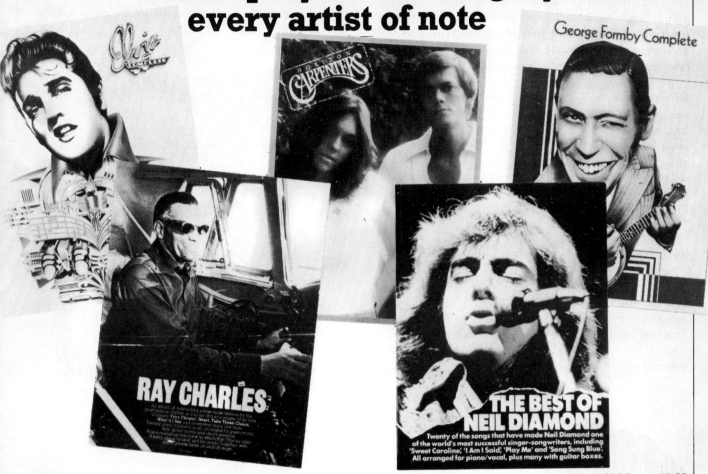

We also publish outstanding tutors for many instruments, both at beginner and advanced level. Listed below is a selection of titles which you are sure to find helpful when looking for suitable music to play, or for a tutor. Order from your local music dealer, Or by post from : Music Sales Ltd., 78 Newman Street, London W.1. When ordering by post, be sure to print your name and address clearly.

Complete Series

Beach Boys Complete	AM	1153D	£3.50
Beatles Complete Guitar	NO	1730C	£3.95
Beatles Complete Piano	NO	1716N	£3.95
Byrds Complete	OK	6232E	£2.95
Cream Complete	AM	1164T	£2.95
Doors Complete	OK	6227P	£2.95
Elvis Complete	AM	1124X	£3.95
George Formby Complete	AM	1247F	£3.95
Herb Albert Complete	AM	1249B	£2.95
Jim Reeves Complete	AM	1365X	£3.95
Rolling Stones Anthology	AM	1143G	£3.95

Groups

Carpenters Song Book Piano/Vocal	AM	1391T	£1.95
All Organ	AM	1466E	£2.50
Chord Organ Editions	AM	1598T	£1.75

Carpenters "Horizon"	AM	1632C	£1.95
Best of the Bee Gees	AM	1471A	£1.75
Yessongs	AM	1163A	£2.95
Completely Free	IS	5144N	£3.00
Mott the Hoople	AM	1467C	£2.50
Roxy Music Songbook	EM	7830B	£1.00
Quadrophenia – The Who	FA	4422T	£3.95

Personality Books

Eric Clapton	AM	1473N	£2.95
Jimi Hendrix	AM	1537N	£3.50
Jim Webb	AM	1491F	£1.95
Ray Charles	AM	1503C	£2.50
Best of Neil Diamond	AM	1504A	£2.50
Songs of David Bowie	AM	1334X	£2.95
Cat Stevens Greatest Hits	IS	5152N	£2.00
Songs of Don McLean	AM	1437A	£2.95
Rod Stewart	AM	1182N	£1.95
Johnny Cash Songbook	OK	6219N	£2.95
Gordon Lightfoot	AM	1155X	£2.50
Gilbert O'Sullivan	AP	3194B	£2.50
Van Morrison Album	KY	1279D	£2.75

Joy Series

Joy of Bach	AM	1095C	£1.50
Joy of Boogie & Blues	MA	1112G	£1.50
Joy of Christmas	AM	1291C	£1.50
Joy of Clarinet	AM	1103N	£1.50
Joy of Classics	AM	1104F	£1.50
Joy of First Year Piano	AM	1290E	£1.50
Joy of Folk Songs	AM	1101A	£1.50
Joy of Guitar	AM	1102T	£1.50
Joy of Jazz	AM	1109G	£1.50

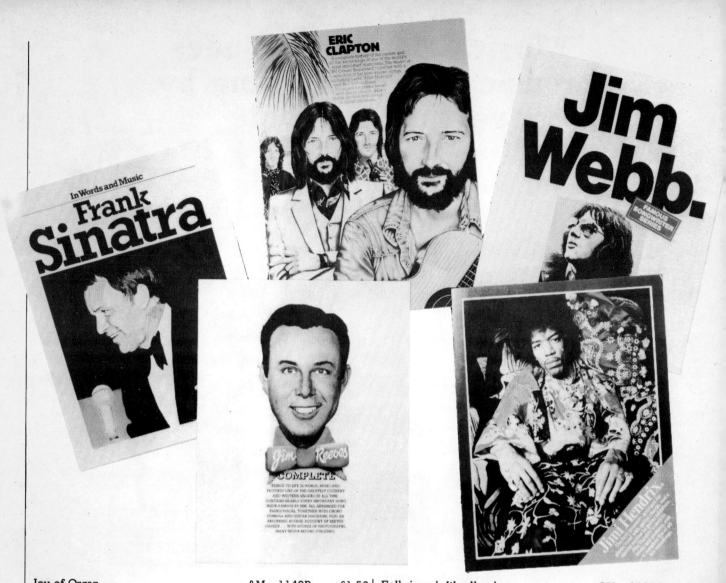

Joy of Organ	AM	1142P	£1.50	Folksinger's Wordbook	OK	6262G	£3.95
Joy of Piano	AM	1105D	£1.50	Solo Guitar Pieces	OK	6280E	£2.50
Joy of Piano Duets	AM	1106B	£1.50	Bluegrass Mandolin	OK	6293G	£2.95
Joy of Recital	AM	1141X	£1.50	The Harp Styles of Sonny Terry	OK	6295C	£2.95
Joy of Song	AM	1140B	£1.50	Jumping, Laughing & Resting	OK	6297T	£1.95
				Love, Work & Hope	OK	6299F	£1.95
In Words And Music Series				Barrelhouse & Boogie Piano	OK	6292P	£2.95
Frank Sinatra	AM	1392N	£1.95				
Tony Bennett	AM	1393F	£1.95	*Chord Organ Albums*			
Nat King Cole	AM	1420G	£1.95	All Our Yesterdays No. 1	AM	1078C	95p
Dean Martin	AM	1394D	£1.95	All Our Yesterdays No. 2	AM	1084N	95p
Perry Como	AM	1469T	£1.95	All Our Yesterdays No. 3	AM	1089P	95p
Andy Williams	AM	1501G	£1.95	All Our Yesterdays No. 4	AM	1090B	95p
Shirley Bassey	AM	1502E	£1.95	All Our Yesterdays No. 5	AM	1296D	95p
Englebert Humperdinck	AM	1587D	£1.95	All Our Yesterdays No. 6	AM	1297B	95p
				All Our Yesterdays No. 7	AM	1298X	95p
Clifford Essex Titles				All Our Yesterdays No. 8	AM	1299P	95p
Music for the Guitar	CL	1021T	95p	All Our Yesterdays No. 9	AM	1300F	95p
Spanish Guitar Tutor	CL	1011B	95p	Beatles to Bacharach	AM	1130E	£1.50
Plectrum Banjo Playing	CL	1010D	95p	Lennon/McCartney 50 Songs	NO	1718D	£1.95
The Banjo and How to Play It	CL	1014G	95p	Music Sales 1st 8 Button Book	AM	1253G	75p
A Variety of Mandolin Music	CL	1032E	95p	Songs of Love	AM	1286G	£1.75
200 Years of Classical Guitar	CL	1020A	£1.95				
Play Country Style Guitar	CL	1005N	95p	*All Organ Albums*			
Chords for Rhythm Guitar	CL	1004T	95p	Lennon/McCartney – 50 Songs	NO	1717F	£2.50
Chords for Plectrum & Tenor Banjo	CL	1003A	95p	Songs of Love	AM	1285P	£2.95
				250 Favourites Series No. 1	AM	1160G	£7.50
Latest Oak Publications				250 Favourites Series No. 2	AM	1373P	£7.50
Blues Harp Songbook	OK	6294E	£2.95	All Organ Album of Pop Hits No. 1	UA	3042C	75p
Slide Guitar	OK	6283T	£2.95	All Organ Album of Pop Hits No. 2	UA	3055E	75p
Folk Guitar Styles of Today	OK	6304F	£2.50	All Organ Album of Film Themes	UA	3041C	75p
Pedal Steel Guitar	OK	6311P	£3.50	Beatles to Bacharach	AM	1132A	£1.75
Bluegrass Banjo	OK	6277E	£2.95	Carpenters	AM	1466E	£2.50